DNA
the Key to Life

Second Edition

Gary Parker
Christian Heritage College

W. Ann Reynolds
University of Illinois
Medical Center

Rex Reynolds
University of Chicago

EMI EDUCATIONAL METHODS / CHICAGO
A DIVISION OF DEVELOPMENT SYSTEMS CORPORATION

ISBN: 0-88462-003-4(1975)

Published by EDUCATIONAL METHODS/Chicago

10   9   8   7   6

Contents

To the Student

The specific performance objectives below were selected and designed with the beginning biology student at the college or high school level in mind. It is hoped that students achieving these cognitive objectives will also achieve the harder-to-measure effective objectives, including: increased interest in DNA, greater awareness of news coverage of related topics, and willingness to participate in discussions of the implications and applications of our growing knowledge and control of DNA. Many references to terms, concepts, and examples encountered in popular literature are included, and several "thought questions" are intended to serve as topics for discussion.

A Unit Quiz is included for evaluation of student achievement of the specific performance objectives.

The overall objectives measured are listed under two headings: (A) Vocabulary and Terminology, and (B) Concepts and Processes. Chapter objectives are also listed in the Introduction to each chapter. Upon completing the program, the beginning college or high school biology student or interested layman should be able to do the following:

A. Vocabulary and Terminology

1. relate these terms to verbal descriptions or diagrams of DNA and protein molecules: polymer, double helix, nucleotide, sugar, phosphate, base, amino acid, amine, acid, R group.
2. recognize a definition of these terms as "DNA language" elements: base, triplet codon, gene, operon, chromosome, genome, and mutation.
3. distinguish between DNA and RNA in terms of double helix vs. single strand, deoxyribose vs. ribose sugar, T vs. U, and deoxyribo- vs. ribonucleic acid.

4. associate the enzymes nuclease, polymerase, and ligase with the rules they play in both replication and repair.
5. identify from verbal descriptions or diagrams the ribosomes and the three kinds of RNA involved in the DNA-protein synthesis process.
6. identify the functions of these proteins: RNA polymerase, activating enzymes, repressors, and incomplete repressors.
7. recognize purine, pyrimidine, guanine, cytosine, adenine, and thymine as terms related to DNA bases.

B. *Concepts and Processes*

8. illustrate the DNA-protein-trait relationship using an example.
9. use a DNA or mRNA "decoder" chart to determine the sequence of amino acids that would be produced by a given sequence of bases.
10. describe base pairing and explain its role in both replication and translation.
11. diagram the pattern of DNA replication and relate the process to base pairing, to the functions of nuclease, polymerase, and ligase enzymes, and to the processes of chromosomal and cellular reproduction.
12. relate nuclease, polymerase, and ligase activity to the DNA repair process, and comment on the significance of this process.
13. identify the roles of mRNA, tRNA, and rRNA in relationship to one another.
14. describe the roles in DNA-protein synthesis of such proteins as RNA polymerase and tRNA-amino acid activating enzymes.
15. describe the roles of repressors and incomplete repressors in "turning DNA on and off."

How to Use This Book

This may be a new type of instructional book for you. The subject matter has been organized (programed) in such a way that the book will be self-instructional. Each frame in the program builds on information you have learned in preceding frames. For that reason it is important that you do not skip around in the program.

Respond at Every Frame

Some frames present new information; others review material presented earlier. Every frame presents a learning situation requiring you to respond.

Once you have written or marked your answer, you will want to find out whether you have responded correctly. The answers are separated from each question by a single line. *Don't look at the correct answer until after you have recorded your answer.*

Use an Answer Mask

To avoid seeing the correct answer inadvertently before recording your own answer, make an Answer Mask by folding an $8\frac{1}{2}''$ x $11''$ piece of paper in half.

As you start a page, cover it with the Answer Mask. Slide the mask down until you see the horizontal line that runs across the entire column. This line separates each frame from its correct answer. Stop moving the mask. Read the frame carefully, then record your answer. Slide the mask down to reveal the correct answer. Then proceed to the next frame.

Review Quizzes and Unit Quiz

At the end of every chapter you will find a short review quiz. Answer all the questions in this section before looking at the correct answers.

I
DNA, PROTEINS, AND HEREDITARY TRAITS

Introduction

Have you ever wondered why your body has developed certain traits? Or why some traits have developed undesirably or failed to develop in some people? For instance, you probably have at least some skin darkening pigment, red blood cells for carrying oxygen, and enzymes for utilizing nutrients in milk. But some people are born lacking skin, hair, or eye color (albinism), having faulty red blood cells that carry oxygen only poorly (sickle cell anemia), or suffering tissue injury from failure to utilize milk sugar (galactosemia).

What, if anything, can be done to correct such hereditary defects? Is it even possible to change the normal reproductive patterns of plants and animals or man? Newspapers, magazines and television are full of reports and stories these days on questions such as these. The search for answers to such questions brings us to two special kinds of molecules, DNA (*d*eoxyribo*n*ucleic *a*cid) and protein. Most of our traits develop under the direct influence of particular kinds of protein molecules. Proteins, in turn, are produced under the influence of DNA.

DNA is called the "key to life" partly because it replicates itself. As a self-reproducing molecule it is copied and passed from generation to generation with its hereditary information.

The relationship of DNA to proteins to traits is characteristic of all life forms (microbes, plants, animals, and man). This all-important DNA-protein-trait relationship, with its many implications, is the subject of this chapter. Upon completing the chapter, you should be able to:

- describe and identify examples of the relationship between DNA, proteins and hereditary traits.

- explain how mutations affect heredity through the DNA-protein-trait relationship.

- relate DNA to the hereditary units called genes and chromosomes.

- comment on man's ability to correct hereditary defects, and even alter the reproductive patterns of life, by using his knowledge of DNA in "genetic engineering."

1.   A clear example of the relationship from DNA to proteins to physical traits is provided by sickle cell anemia, an inheritable blood disease. The illustrations below show magnified red blood cells from a normal person, a person with sickle cell trait, and a person with sickle cell anemia at its worst.

RED BLOOD CELLS FROM PERSONS WITH . . .

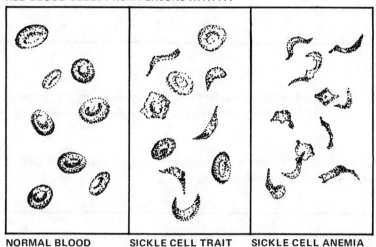

NORMAL BLOOD   SICKLE CELL TRAIT   SICKLE CELL ANEMIA

a.   Which blood sample shown above contains the highest number of smoothly rounded red cells? _____

b.   Which sample contains jagged-edged, half-moon or sickle-shaped cells, and no round cells? _____

c.   When blood flows through the smallest blood vessels, the red cells often have to squeeze through single file. Blood cells from which sample above would probably slide through most easily? _____ Which would most likely snag and perhaps block the blood flow if forced into narrow vessels? _____

_____

a. normal;   b. sickle cell anemia;   c. normal; sickle cell anemia

3

2. A person with sickle cell trait usually does not encounter major difficulties because of the slight red blood cell abnormality. But, under certain conditions, the red cells of a person with sickle cell anemia may snag and block the flow of blood through small vessels. The vital oxygen-carrying function of these red cells is severely reduced. What physical trait is responsible for the abnormal behavior of sickle cells—their size, shape, or weight?

shape

---

shape

3. Red blood cells are packed full of oxygen-carrying protein molecules called hemoglobin (about 280 million molecules per cell).

Do you think differences in hemoglobin could produce differences in red blood cell shape? *yes*

---

yes (just as changing the shape of a child's blocks might make it hard to build a square house)

4. Hemoglobin, like all other protein molecules, is composed of a chain of amino acids. The diagrams below represent a portion of the amino acid chain in normal hemoglobin (HbA) and the corresponding portion of the amino acid chain in sickle cell hemoglobin (HbS):

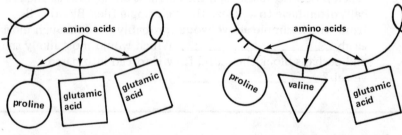

NORMAL ADULT HEMOGLOBIN (HbA)   SICKLE CELL HEMOGLOBIN (HbS)

4

a. Compare the three amino acids in the diagramed portions of normal and sickle cell hemoglobin. Are the amino acids at the left in each diagram the same? _yes_ Are the amino acids at the center of each diagram the same? _no_ Are the amino acids at the right of each diagram the same? _yes_

b. Judging from your answers to question *a*, are the amino acid sequences in normal and sickle cell hemoglobin the same or different? _diff_

c. Has your brief look at the structure of hemoglobin molecules supported or denied the suspicion that differences in red cell shapes might be caused by differences in the cells' protein molecules? _yes - supported_

---

a. yes; no (glutamic amino acid in one, valine in the other); yes;
b. different; c. supported

5. "Differences in particular physical traits can often be traced to differences in particular kinds of protein molecules." Explain how sickle cell anemia provides an example to support this concept.

SCA — diff shapes of RBC's can be correlated to diff in Hgb, structure of RBC's

---

Sample answer: In sickle cell anemia, a difference in the shapes of red blood cells can be related to differences in the hemoglobin molecules of the blood cells.

NOTE: At various times in the program, you will be asked to express ideas in your own words. In such cases, compare your answer with the sample answer provided. Look for main points; differences in detail and grammar are expected.

6. Generalize from the sickle cell anemia example, and write a sentence expressing the relationship between *traits* and *proteins*.

SCAT can be caused
by diff Hg-molecular
structure

Sample answer: Hereditary traits are often derived from or caused by particular protein molecules.

7. Hair is composed of dead cells packed full of the protein keratin.

a. On the basis of the generalization you made in frame 6, would you expect straight and curly hair to contain the same kind of keratin? ___no___

---

no

8. There are two kinds of keratin, as shown below.

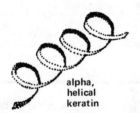

alpha,
helical
keratin

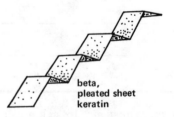

beta,
pleated sheet
keratin

Curly hair contains alpha keratin, which has a helical structure, and straight hair contains beta keratin, which has a pleated structure. Is such a difference in keratin what you expected? ___yes___

---

yes

9.

Disease or Abnormal Condition	Missing or Defective Protein
albinism	tyrosinase
galactosemia	galactose transferase
glycogen storage disease I	glucose-1-phosphatase
hemophilia A	clotting factor VIII
PKU (phenyl ketonuria)	phenylalanine hydroxylase
sickle cell anemia	hemoglobin
Tay-Sach's Disease	hexosaminidase

The chart above lists several disease conditions in human beings, each of which can be traced to a defect or loss in some specific protein.

a. Very rarely, a newborn will develop severe tissue injury because his body is unable to utilize a milk sugar, galactose, and prevent its buildup in the blood. What protein normally prevents the harmful excess of circulating galactose, called galactosemia? *galactose transferase*

b. Lack of what protein causes the absence of skin, hair, and eye coloration, a condition called albinism? *tyrosinase*

c. What general rule is illustrated by the chart above? *disease* 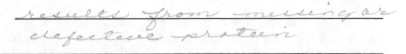 *results from missing or defective protein*

---

a. galactose transferase;   b. tyrosinase;   c. *Sample answer:* Physical traits, in this case disease conditions, are related to particular proteins.

7

10. Given that particular proteins produce particular traits, the next question becomes, "What produces proteins?"

Viruses have helped to answer this question. Many viruses consist of just two kinds of molecules: (1) protein molecules forming an outer coat, and (2) DNA (*deoxyribonucleic acid*) molecules forming an inner core. Label these two kinds of molecules on the different types of viruses diagramed below.

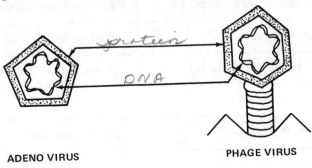

ADENO VIRUS   PHAGE VIRUS

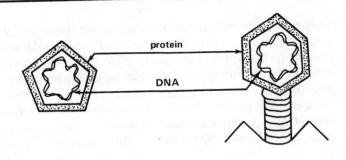

11. Phage viruses attack bacterial cells. The sequence of steps in this attack is shown in the diagram at the top of the next page. (1) Phage DNA is injected into the bacterial cells, but the protein coat remains outside. (2) Shortly afterward, the bacterial cell fills up with 200 to 300 complete new virus particles with both DNA cores and protein coats. (3) Finally, the cell ruptures and newly formed viruses are released.

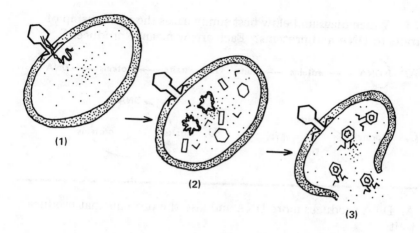

(1)

(2)

(3)

a. Do these observations suggest that the viral protein coat is produced under the direction of viral protein or under the direction of viral DNA? _V. DNA_

b. These observations also tell us something about the production of DNA. Is the viral DNA produced under the direction of viral protein or under the direction of viral DNA? _V. DNA_

c. Which statement below best summarizes the implications of phage virus studies? _3_

    (1) Proteins produce DNA.
    (2) DNA produces protein.
    (3) DNA produces both protein and additional DNA.

---

a. viral DNA;   b. viral DNA;   c. (3)

12. These virus studies have shown that proteins are produced by _DNA_ molecules, and that DNA molecules are produced by _DNA_ molecules.

DNA; DNA

13. Which diagram below best summarizes the relationship of traits to DNA and proteins? Each arrow means "produces."

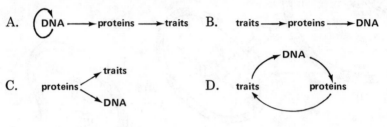

A. DNA produces more DNA and also the proteins that produce traits.

14. Apply your understanding of the DNA-protein-trait relationship diagramed above by marking the following T if probably true, or F if probably false.

_T_ a. Ultraviolet light is known to cause changes (mutations) in DNA, so skin cells overexposed to the ultraviolet light in sunlight could develop changed proteins and traits.

_F_ b. A man or woman can exercise and develop large muscles, and this trait can cause changes in muscle protein and DNA.

_T_ c. *S* bacteria have a protective capsule and can cause pneumonia, but *R* bacteria of the same type have no protective capsule and are harmless. DNA extracted from *S* bacteria, however, could enable *R* bacteria to form a capsule and cause pneumonia.

_T_ d. If scientists could change the DNA in the cells of a given life form, they could change—for good or ill—the proteins and the traits that the life form possesses.

a. T (Ultraviolet overdose can, in fact, cause skin cell changes resulting in cancer. The DNA is affected first, then proteins, then traits.) b. F (Acquired characteristics, such as enlarged muscle fibers, have no effect on DNA and are thus not heritable. Years

DNA → proteins → traits - (handwritten, top margin)

ago, people thought that traits acquired by exercise, etc., could be transmitted to offspring.)   c. T (The transformation by DNA of harmless R bacteria into pneumonia-causing S bacteria was an early evidence of DNA's importance.)   d. T (Scientists, philosophers and ethicists are exploring the potentials for good or ill of "genetic engineering," or man's ability to regulate DNA.)

15.   To review, draw a diagram describing the relationship of hereditary traits to DNA and protein molecules, then write a sentence expressing your thoughts in words.

DNA → proteins → traits (handwritten)

DNA reproduces itself & also produces various proteins & physical traits of an organism (handwritten)

Sample answer: DNA molecules produce *protein* molecules which, in turn, produce hereditary *traits*, and DNA also produces additional DNA molecules, or

DNA ⟶ proteins ⟶ traits

16.   In viruses and bacteria, DNA is present as a circular molecule. In plant and animal cells, DNA is found in chromosomes which are long, coiled, thread-like structures found in the cell's nucleus. Use this knowledge that DNA is found in chromosomes in a cell's nucleus to reason out the answer to the question given at the top of the next page.

11

The sperm cell of sea urchin species B (*psammechinus*) was used to fertilize an egg cell of species A (*sphaerechinus*) from which the nucleus had been removed.

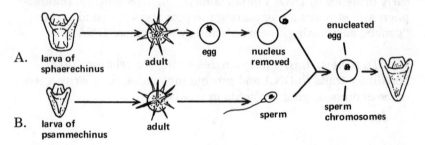

A. larva of sphaerechinus → adult → egg → nucleus removed → enucleated egg

B. larva of psammechinus → adult → sperm → sperm chromosomes

Did the larva that developed from an A cell with a B nucleus have the traits of species A or B or some of the traits of both?

_____*B*_____

---

characteristics of B (This experiment has been performed and confirms that DNA is the carrier of hereditary information.)

17.

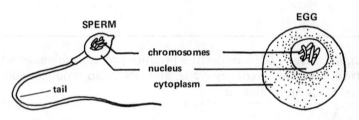

SPERM — chromosomes — nucleus — cytoplasm — tail

EGG

A human being starts life as a single cell formed by the fusion of an egg and a sperm cell. The sperm cell contributes 23 chromosomes to the fertilized egg's 23 chromosomes. A human child inherits from his parents (check one):

_____a. traits
_____b. proteins for producing traits
__✓_c. DNA for producing proteins for producing traits

c

NOTE: More information about the movement of chromosomes
from one generation to the next is found in two other books by
the authors in the Programmed Biology Series, *Mitosis and Meiosis*
(Chicago: Educational Methods, 1968), and *Heredity* (Chicago:
Educational Methods, 1970).

18. The sperm cell is much smaller than the egg cell, which contributes most of the molecules found in the fertilized egg. Both
sperm and egg cells contribute 23 chromosomes, however. Is the
child that develops likely to show more of its female parent's
traits, more of the male's, or about equal proportions of each?
_____*equal*_____

---

about equal   (It is primarily the DNA, contributed equally by each
parent through their 23 chromosomes, that molds the traits of the
child, although a few, minor traits are traceable to effects of other
molecules in the female's egg.)

19. Most human beings have cells with 46 chromosomes, but
occasionally people have only 45 or 47. Would you expect such
persons to differ markedly from the general population or not?
_____*differ*_____

---

probably differ (For example, persons with a cluster of mental
defects, including a form of mental retardation called Down's
Syndrome, have an extra chromosome numbered 21.)

20. The previous frames gave several examples of the relationship
of hereditary traits to chromosomes in the nucleus of the cell.
What kind of molecules within chromosomes are responsible for
heredity? _____*DNA*_____

DNA

21. Below is a "map" of a fruit fly chromosome.

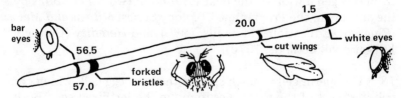

Genetic studies have shown that certain segments of the chromosome, called *genes*, are related to certain traits.

a. From what you have learned, it seems likely that genes are composed of what kind of molecule? ___DNA___

b. Genes are related to traits. What you have learned, however, suggests that genes do not produce traits directly, but instead produce the molecules which produce traits, namely ___protein___ molecules.

c. What word meets this definition: "a segment of chromosomal DNA responsible for producing the protein related to development of a specific trait"? ___genes___

---

a. DNA;   b. protein;   c. gene

22. Diagramed below is the map of a structure extracted from the nucleus of a tomato cell.

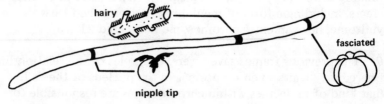

a. What is this structure called? ___chromosome___

b. What kind of substance would be found in this kind of struc-
    ture and practically nowhere else in the cell? __DNA__
c. What name is given to the segments of this structure that are
    related to the development of a specific trait, such as a hairy
    stem or nipple tip tomato? *genes*
d. What molecules, which give rise to specific traits, are produced
    by the gene segments above? *proteins*

---

a. chromosome; b. DNA; c. genes; d. protein molecules

23. Hereditary factors are responsible for the development of
certain traits. What are such hereditary factors called? *genes*
What kind of molecules make up these hereditary factors?
__DNA__

---

genes; DNA

24. Write a paragraph and compose a diagram summarizing the
relationship among the following: DNA, proteins, traits, genes,
and chromosomes.

*Genes are segments of the
DNA chromosome which
produce protein & ultimately
produce specific traits*

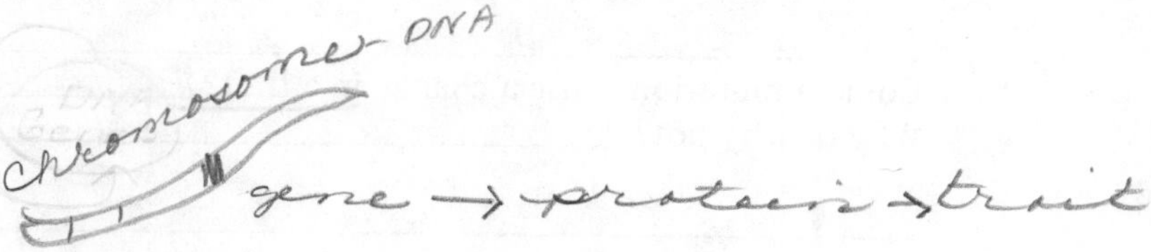

chromosome DNA

gene → protein → trait

Sample answer: Genes are segments of DNA molecules contained in chromosomes. Genes produce the proteins responsible for development of hereditary traits.

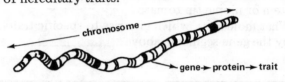

25.

When a cell prepares to reproduce, each chromosome makes a copy of itself. The ability of chromosomes to reproduce is based on the ability of DNA molecules to make ___DNA___ molecules.

DNA

26. The structure of DNA molecules can be altered by agents such as radiation and certain chemicals. These changes are called *mutations*.

a. Are radiation or chemically induced mutations in DNA likely to be hereditary? __yes__ Why or why not? _____
mutated DNA could reproduce itself

b. Could a mutation cause a change in a trait? __yes__
Why or why not? _____
change DNA → change protein → change trait

16

a. yes; *Sample answer:* because DNA produces more DNA when chromosomes duplicate in cell reproduction, and the mutated DNA would probably duplicate as mutated DNA   b. yes; *Sample answer:* because mutated DNA would produce altered proteins which could, if the alterations were great enough, produce trait changes. (Incidentally, the majority of mutations are tiny ones and are not reflected in major trait changes.)

27.

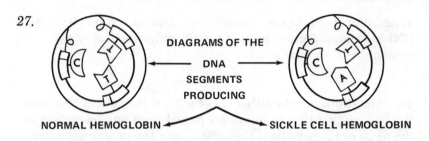

Diagramed above, in a highly schematic way, are portions of two DNA molecules, one related to normal hemoglobin and the other to sickle cell hemoglobin.

a. In the two DNA molecules above, are the sequences of sub-units labeled C, T, and A the same? _____

b. Would the proteins produced by these two DNA molecules likely be the same? _____

c. Would the shapes of red blood cells containing the protein produced by these DNA molecules be the same? _____

d. Does the data you just reviewed suggest that the hereditary disease sickle cell anemia may have started as a mutation in DNA? _____

a. no;   b. no;   c. probably not (Not all changes in hemoglobin change the red blood cell shape, but some do.)   d. yes (At least, mutations are often considered to be the causes of hereditary diseases such as sickle cell anemia.)

28. It is now generally accepted that many of the hereditary diseases related to defects in one protein arose originally as changes in DNA molecules.

a. What are such changes in DNA called? *mutations*
b. What factors can cause such changes in DNA?
     radiation
     chemicals

---

a. mutations;   b. *Sample answer:* radiation or certain chemicals (Other biologic factors, not yet clearly understood, may also be responsible for mutations.)

29. Mutations may be either (1) *genetic*, if they affect reproductive cells so that the mutations are passed from one generation to the next, or (2) *somatic* if they affect only the nonreproductive cells in individuals and are not transmitted from one generation to the next. Mark the following as most likely examples of either genetic or somatic mutations.

___1___ a. Sickle cell anemia apparently arose among Africans, where sickle cell trait confers some resistance to deadly malaria, and it is found most often today among persons of African descent.

___2___ b. An increased risk of skin cancer is found among persons who consistently overexpose themselves to the tanning rays of the sun.

___1___ c. Although hemophilia, or "bleeder's disease," was not reported among her ancestors, descendants of the British Queen Victoria have exhibited an unusually high incidence of the disease.

___1___ d. Tay-Sach's disease, a disease attributable to a defect in one protein, is most common among people of Jewish descent and seems to have arisen in a Jewish community in Czeckoslovakia.

___2___ e. Blood forming cells are particularly susceptible to radiation. Before the hazards of radiation were appreciated,

workers who painted radium numbers on watch faces were
more likely than the general population to develop cancers
of the blood (leukemias).

---

a. genetic;   b. somatic;   c. genetic;   d. genetic;   e. somatic

30. We know that such "blind" forces in nature as radiation can
produce mutations in DNA, and that the vast majority of these
mutations are harmful. Does it seem possible, however, that
scientists might be able to produce mutations in DNA deliberately,
seeking beneficial effects or at least the correction of defective
DNA? _yes_

"Yes" is the optimistic answer. Scientists are presently able to
induce mutations in DNA in lower forms of life with the hope
that, ultimately, defects in DNA can be corrected.

31. "Genetic engineering" is the name given to attempts at im-
proving or correcting heredity by making deliberate changes in
DNA.

a.   If an organism's DNA molecules are changed, what other
     molecules will be changed? _protein_
b.   If these molecules are changed, what else about the organism
     will be changed? _traits_
c.   Could changes in the DNA of reproductive cells induced by
     geneticists or genetic engineers affect future generations of
     that organism? _yes_

---

a. proteins;   b. physical or hereditary traits;   c. Yes, changes in
the DNA of reproductive cells could affect future generations.

32. Some babies are born with an inability to produce the protein galactose transferase, so that the galactose accumulation from milk causes them to have a condition called galactosemia. How might a geneticist hope to treat this disease?

_____a. Keep the baby on a milk-free diet, since milk is the main source of galactose.

_____b. Inject the baby with the transferase protein.

__✓__c. Use a virus with transferase-producing DNA to infect human cells.

---

c might be the future choice of a geneticist, but compare a with c and b:

c. This strange use of virus DNA has been suggested by geneticists and *it has been done*, to a limited extent. A group of scientists recently infected human cells in *tissue culture* (*not* in a human being) with a viral DNA that enabled the cells to make and keep making transferase protein. Geneticists place much hope in artificial or man-made viruses, but they also know such viruses may have harmful side effects.

a. Avoiding milk is the simplest procedure, and is actually carried out effectively, although it avoids, rather than treats, the disease, and is unrelated to "genetic engineering."

b. Protein injections would have to be made over and over (since proteins do not reproduce themselves), and proteins can also cause allergic reactions.

33. Suppose a scientist wanted to grow many identical twin frogs. Could he take the DNA in the nuclei of cells from one donor frog, inject the nuclei into egg cells whose DNA had been removed, and grow a cluster of frogs identical to the donor? _yes_____

---

yes—Strange as it may sound, this *has been done*, and the technique is called *cloning*. Some see advantages in cloning (e.g., growing skin for transplantation onto burn victims), but others see frightening possibilities (e.g., making identical twin humans to run identical machines, as suggested in Aldous Huxley's *Brave New World*).

34. The new life science whose goal is to correct hereditary defects and/or improve the general hereditary traits of man and other life forms is called *genetic engineering.* The focus of attention in this endeavor is the molecule responsible for producing proteins and traits, namely ____*DNA*____.

---

genetic engineering; DNA

35. Two techniques presently available to geneticists are (1) controlled viruses, and (2) cloning.

a. Which of these techniques was used to cure galactosemia in human tissue culture cells by introducing the correct DNA?
____*1*____

b. Which technique often involves nuclear transplantation and the production of multiple copies of a single cell type?
____*2*____

---

a. controlled viruses;   b. cloning

36. In addition to using viruses and cloning to alter the DNA of a cell, geneticists could use a "shotgun" approach. They could bombard cells with radiation, such as x-rays, gamma rays, or ultraviolet light, and look for favorable changes. What would such radiation do to cells?

____*change DNA — change protein*____

____" *traits*____

Sample answer: Radiation causes changes called mutations in DNA, and these changes result in altered proteins and traits. The geneticist hopes to find and select some favorable changes. (This technique has been successful in producing new strains of antibiotic-producing fungi.)

37. Some viruses are involved in these processes: (1) *transduction,* in which a virus acts to carry a gene from one bacterium to another, and (2) *lysogeny,* in which viral DNA fuses with the chromosomal DNA of a plant, animal, or microbial cell and multiplies with it. What value might a geneticist see in these two processes?

viruses can be used to transmit genetic material in DNA to specific cells.

Sample answer: In both transduction and lysogeny, viruses are acting to transmit genetic material. The geneticist might hope to provide such viruses with specific genes and direct them to carry the DNA within specific cells.

38. The focus of interest for geneticists is, of course, the *gene.*

a. A gene is usually a segment of what larger structure?
   chromosome
b. What kind of molecule makes up a gene? _____ *DNA* _____
c. What kind of molecules are produced by genes? *protein*
d. Generally speaking, what are the results of the molecules produced by genes? *traits*
e. What molecule's ability to produce more of itself makes it possible for genes to reproduce themselves? _____ *DNA* _____
f. What effect do radiation and certain chemicals have on genes? *cause mutations*

22

a. chromosomes;   b. DNA;   c. proteins;   d. *Sample answer:* physical or hereditary traits;   e. DNA;   f. *Sample answer:* They cause mutations—changes in DNA which may cause changes in proteins and traits.

39. Between genes and genetic traits stand protein molecules, the molecules produced by genes that are responsible for genetic traits. Match the proteins at right below with their associated traits.

_b_(1)   sickle cell anemia   a.   keratin
_a_(2)   curly hair   b.   hemoglobin
_d_(3)   albinism, or lack of skin,   c.   galactose transferase
          hair, and eye color.   d.   tyrosinase
_c_(4)   galactosemia

---

(1) b;   (2) a;   (3) d;   (4) c

40. The molecule that provides genes with their genetic or hereditary significance is DNA.

a.   Use sickle cell anemia to describe the relationship between an inherited trait, protein, and DNA.

DNA of gene of chromosome
for hemoglobin of RRC altered
producing "   " protein
& sickle cell trait.
Alterations passed on

b. Indicate how geneticists might one day attempt to treat or
    cure this disease.

Lysogeny could be used
where viral DNA fuses
a chromosomal DNA
to alter this gene

Sample answers: a. In sickle cell anemia, the abnormal, sickle
shape of red blood cells is related to the abnormal structure of the
hemoglobin within the red cells. The hemoglobin abnormality, in
turn, is related to a change or defect in the DNA molecule in the
gene responsible for hemoglobin production. Radiation or some
other factor may have caused the first mutation in some reproductive cell, and the trait was then passed on by DNA through suc-
ceeding generations. b. Geneticists might hope one day to re-
move the defective DNA in hemoglobin producing cells and
"splice in" the correct DNA, perhaps using controlled viruses as
DNA carriers. Success has already been achieved in using viral
DNA to alter protein in cells with the galactosemia trait in human
tissue culture. Many technical difficulties remain, but you will
undoubtedly be reading more about genetic engineering in the
next few years.

Summary

This chapter introduced the concept that specific traits are derived from specific protein molecules which, in turn, are related to specific DNA molecules in chromosome segments called genes. You learned, for example, how curliness of hair is related to the protein keratin produced by a specific gene. You also learned how changes or mutations in DNA caused by radiation or certain chemicals can produce hereditary defects by altering or preventing the production of certain proteins. Tyrosinase and galactose transferase proteins are lacking in albinism and galactosemia, respectively, and hemoglobin is altered from normal to sickle cell type by mutated DNA.

Finally, if newspapers, magazines, and television had not already done so, this chapter introduced you to the prospect that geneticists might one day be able to use their knowledge of the DNA-protein-trait relationship to correct hereditary defects, and, more debatably, to alter the characteristics of selected life forms and their normal patterns of reproduction.

Review Quiz

1. Match each of the following traits with the factor responsible
    for producing it:

    b (1) curly hair   *c* (3) albinism
    a (2) sickle cell anemia   *d* (4) galactosemia

    a. mutant gene producing improperly shaped hemoglobin
       within red blood cells
    b. gene producing the protein keratin, in the beta or pleated
       form
    c. mutant DNA failing to produce the protein tyrosinase
       which makes melanin, the skin, hair, and eye pigment
    d. mutant DNA failing to produce transferase, a blood
       protein needed to keep the milk sugar galactose from
       accumulating and causing tissue injury

2. In your own words, describe the relationship of hereditary
    traits to DNA and protein molecules, and give one example
    to illustrate what you mean.

    DNA of chromosomal genes which
    contains specific info. on certain
    traits. Then DNA altered
    by rad, chem. or other means,
    alter → altered protein
    → "traits.

3. DNA molecules are found in the cell's nucleus in long,
    thread-like structures called *chromosomes* The segment
    of this structure responsible for producing the protein related
    to one specific trait is called a _gene_.

4. What are mutations, and why are they important? *random alterations in DNA molecule*

5. What is genetic engineering, and what kinds of things might this aspect of genetics one day accomplish?
    attempts to improve or change DNA to alter hereditary traits

    - elim. specific hered. disease

Check your answers against those on page 143.

II
THE STRUCTURE AND
LANGUAGE OF DNA

Introduction

The previous chapter suggested that understanding the synthesis
and regulation of DNA may one day enable scientists to cure
hereditary defects and even alter the hereditary makeup of life.
DNA has extraordinary potential, because it stores information
for making two kinds of molecules: (1) more DNA, the basis of
all reproduction and heredity, and (2) proteins, the molecules
that link DNA with the actual expression of hereditary traits.

DNA's ability to direct the production of more of both DNA
and protein is an excellent example of the relationship of structure to function. The structure of DNA molecules gives them an
information-carrying capacity something like the English language.
Upon completing this chapter, you should be able to:

- describe the structural features of DNA molecules (using
  such terms as double helix, polymer, nucleotide, sugar, phosphate, and base).

- describe the structural features of protein molecules (using
  such terms as amino acid and R group).

- relate the structure of DNA to the "language of life" that
  carries information for making DNA and proteins—the bases
  of reproduction and hereditary development in all known
  life forms.

41.

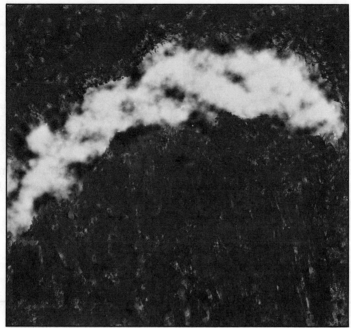

Above is an actual photograph of a DNA molecule, magnified 7,300,000 times by means of an electron microscope. In the photograph, the DNA molecule looks like (check one):

___✓_a. two strands of rope twisted around each other in a spiral
_____b. a series of railroad boxcars
_____c. a picket fence

---

a

42. The spiral formed by DNA strands is called a helix. Since two strands are involved, is DNA better called a single helix or a double helix? _double helix_

---

double helix

43.

 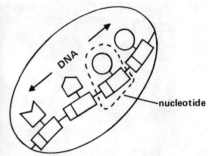

nucleotide

A double helix includes two strands of DNA. Each strand is made up of a series of units called *nucleotides*. A nucleotide is to a DNA strand, then, as:

_____a. a cup is to a saucer
__✓__b. a pearl is to a pearl necklace
_____c. a hammer is to an anvil

---

b (A nucleotide is to DNA as a pearl is to a pearl necklace.)

44.   A chain of many chemical segments is called a *polymer* (*poly*-many; *mer*-segments), and one link in the chain is called a *monomer* (*mono*-one). In the case of DNA and nucleotides, then, which is the polymer? ___*DNA*___ Which is the monomer? *nucleotide*

DNA; nucleotides

45.   DNA stands for deoxyribo*nucleic* acid. The second half of this name refers to DNA being found primarily in the cell's nucleus. The same root is used in naming DNA monomers, which are _N_ _U_ _C_ _L_ _E_ otides.

---

*nucleo*tides

nucleotide = monomer
Dna   = polymer

46. A nucleotide is one link or monomer in a DNA chain. In turn, each nucleotide consists of three parts:

(1) a *base* group that protrudes from the side of the DNA chain,
(2) a *sugar* group attached to the base, and
(3) a *phosphate* group joining the sugar of one nucleotide to the sugar of the next nucleotide, forming a "backbone" from which the bases protrude.

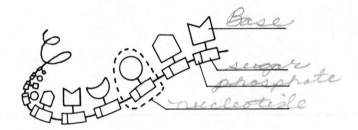

Base
sugar
phosphate
nucleotide

Using this verbal description, first label the nucleotide, then label the base, sugar, and phosphate parts of a nucleotide on the DNA polymer above.

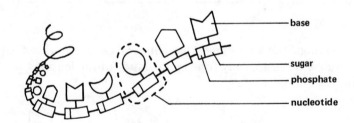

base

sugar
phosphate
nucleotide

47. A nucleotide consists of sugar, phosphate, and base groups.

a. Which two of these three parts of nucleotides form the "backbone" of a DNA polymer? _sugar_ , _phosphate_
Which part protrudes from the side of the chain? _base_

b. Join the four nucleotide monomers below to form a short DNA polymer.

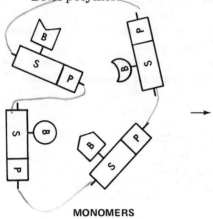

MONOMERS   POLYMER

a. sugar, phosphate (either order); base; b. *Sample answer:*
(The ⬚S⬚P⬚—⬚S⬚P⬚ backbone is necessary; any sequence of bases and orientation that includes this backbone is acceptable.)

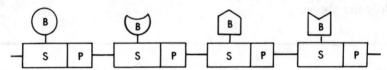

48. Although DNA polymers typically consist of *thousands* of nucleotides, there are only *four* major kinds of nucleotides, as diagramed below:

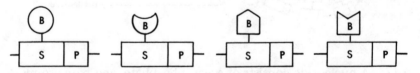

a. According to the diagrams, all nucleotides have the same sugar and phosphate groups. What group makes each of the four major kinds of nucleotides different from one another?
       base

b. What feature of this group makes it different in each of the four major kinds of nucleotides? *shape or structure*

---

a. base;   b. *Sample answers:* shape or structure

49. The diagram below compares a DNA molecule with an ink stamp used to label mail. Complete the comparison by matching the numbered and lettered items.

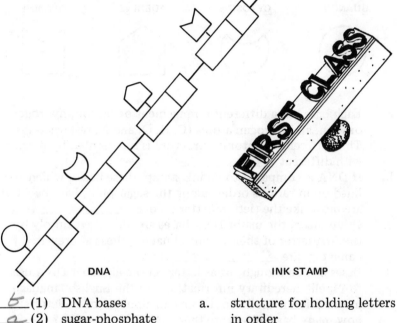

DNA   INK STAMP

_b_ (1) DNA bases   a. structure for holding letters
_a_ (2) sugar-phosphate   in order
         backbone   b. sequence of different letters
                                        spelling out the information,
                                        "FIRST CLASS"

---

(1) b;   (2) a   (The sugar-phosphate backbone is like a type holder, and the bases are like letters held in proper sequence along the holder.)

50. Shown below are names, chemical formulas, and simple diagrams for each of the four different bases of DNA:

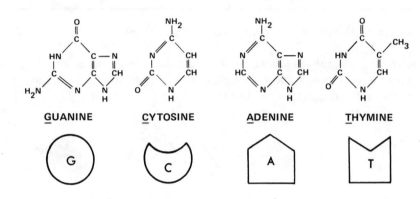

GUANINE   CYTOSINE   ADENINE   THYMINE

G   C   A   T

a. Each base has a different arrangement of carbon, hydrogen, oxygen, and nitrogen atoms (C, H, O, and N, respectively). This difference in atomic structure is represented by diagrams with different ~~structure / shapes~~.
b. If DNA is compared to an ink stamp, these bases, which are lined up in various orders along the sugar-phosphate backbone, are most like the (letters/letter holder) ~~letters~~.
c. Quite often, the major DNA bases are identified simply by the first letter of their chemical names; these abbreviated name tags are _G_, _C_, _A_, and _T_.
d. Bases can be thought of as letters in the alphabet DNA uses to "spell" hereditary information. In the English language, information is spelled out using an alphabet of 26 letters; how many base letters are there in DNA's alphabet? ~~4~~

---

a. *Sample answers:* shapes or structures   b. letters   c. G, C, A, T (any order)   d. four (4)

51. DNA makes both protein and more DNA. The information for making both kinds of molecules is "spelled out" in a series of chemical groups protruding from the DNA polymers. What are these groups that are used to spell hereditary information called? _bases_ These groups are held in place like letters in an ink stamp by DNA's "backbone," which is formed by what two groups? _sugars_ and _phosphates_

---

bases; sugar and phosphate (either order)

52. DNA may be represented by either a block diagram or a lettered line diagram:

In the lettered line diagram:

a. the letters G, C, A, and T represent the parts of DNA nucleotides called _bases_ ;
b. the line represents the backbone composed of the groups called _sugars_ and _phosphate_; and
c. a unit that includes all three of the groups is called a _nucleotide_

---

a. bases   b. sugar and phosphate (either order)   c. nucleotide

53.

A DNA gene is like a sentence specifying production of a particular protein. What are the letters used to write these DNA sentences? _bases_

DNA gene = sentence
Bases = letters

bases (or nucleotides; The bases are the distinguishing features of the nucleotides, since the sugars and phosphates are all alike.)

54.   Here comes the *J*udge.
                            Here comes the *F*udge.

Changing letters in an English sentence can change its meaning. Changing base letters in a DNA sentence would (check the most complete answer):

_____a. change the protein molecule produced by the changed DNA
_____b. change the trait that depended on the protein produced by DNA
_____c. possibly change the DNA of future generations, since the changed DNA would produce more changed DNA
__✓__d. produce changes in proteins, traits, and possibly even the DNA of future generations, since all of these are related

---

d

55.   **NORMAL BLOOD**   **SICKLE CELL ANEMIA**

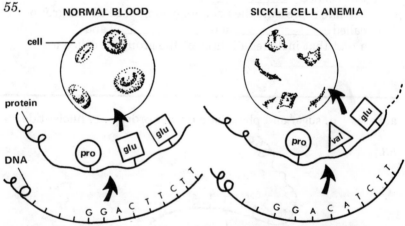

The "sickle cell anemia story" is reviewed above. DNA bases *indirectly* control the production of protein, working through RNA. RNA's role will be covered in a later chapter.

a. Are there visible differences in the traits of red blood cells taken from persons with normal blood and those with sickle cell anemia? _____yes_____ Are there differences in the hemoglobin molecules found in these red cells? _____yes_____ Are there differences in the DNA molecules specifying production of these proteins? _____yes_____

b. What does the diagram above suggest to you concerning the effect of changes in DNA on related proteins and traits?
_____ are _____

_____

_____

c. What are changes in the sequence of bases along DNA called? _mutations_ Name one factor that can cause such changes.
radiation

d. If scientists could somehow change the DNA gene responsible for the sickle cell trait to a normal form, could they prevent this hereditary disease? _____yes_____ What name is given to the relatively new science dealing with such problems?
genetic engineering

_____

a. yes (cell shape); yes (val vs. glu in middle position); yes (A vs. T in middle position);   b. *Sample answer:* Changes in DNA also cause changes in proteins and traits.   c. mutations; *Sample answer:* radiation, or certain chemicals;   d. Yes, although it should be borne in mind that these achievements in *genetic engineering* lie far off in the future.

56. What is the importance of the sequence of bases along a DNA molecule, and what is the importance of changes in the DNA base sequence?
of DNA
seq. spells out info on
hereditary trait - change
pro & trait

Sample answer: The sequence of bases along a DNA molecule "spells out" hereditary information, causing the production of proteins and their related traits. Changes in the DNA base sequence can change the hereditary traits of an organism.

57. DNA produces traits by producing (or, more precisely, by specifying the production of) particular proteins. Molecules of DNA and protein are each chains of repeated units, so DNA and protein molecules are both (monomers/polymers) _____*poly*_____ and the units comprising them are (monomers/polymers) _____*mono*_____ .

---

polymers; monomers

58.

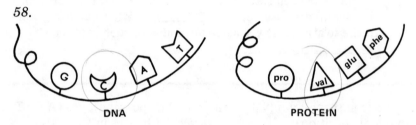

DNA   PROTEIN

DNA molecules are polymers of *nucleotides* and proteins are polymers of *amino acids*. Circle and label a nucleotide and an amino acid on the diagrams above.

Sample answer:

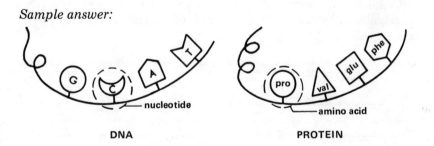

nucleotide   amino acid

DNA   PROTEIN

38

59.

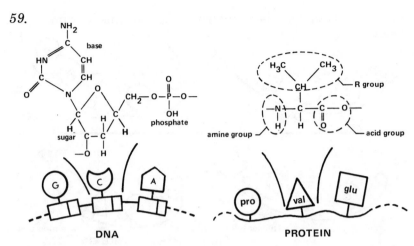

DNA   **PROTEIN**

Just as the nucleotide segments of DNA each have three parts, the amino acid segments of proteins each have three parts.

a.   Which two parts of the nucleotide monomers form the backbone of a DNA polymer? _sugar_ and _phosphate_. Which part of the nucleotide protrudes from the side of the polymer chain? _base_

b.   As the diagrams above indicate, amino acids form protein polymers in much the same way as nucleotides form DNA. Which two parts of the amino acid monomers form the backbone of protein polymers? _amine_ and _acid_ Which part of the amino acid protrudes from the side of the polymer chain? _R_

Answers are presented in chart form, as a memory aid.

a. DNA:	*sugar* and *phosphate* backbone	*base* side groups
b. protein:	*amine* and *acid* backbone	*R* side groups

60.   The backbone of a protein molecule is made up of *amine* and *acid* groups, and for this reason the monomers of protein polymers are called _amino acids_.

---

amino acids

61. Identify and label each polymer and monomer diagramed below:

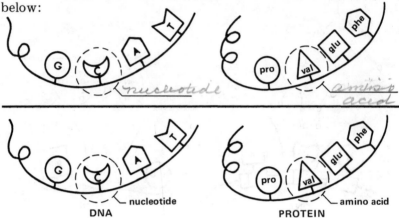

nucleotide   *amino*
                      acid

nucleotide   amino acid
DNA   **PROTEIN**

62. All amino acids have the same amine and acid groups, but there are about 20 different R groups making 20 different kinds of amino acids. Label the R groups on the protein diagramed below: *R - groups*

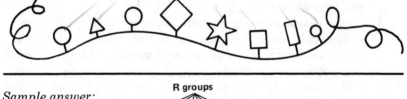

Sample answer:
                R groups

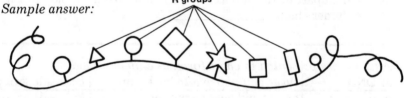

63. Although there can be minor variations, basically four different kinds of nucleotides and 20 different kinds of amino acids are found in cells.

a.   An English sentence may consist of many letters in total, but these long sentences are composed of only 26 different kinds

40

of letters. A typical DNA polymer consists of thousands of monomers. These long molecules are composed of how many different kinds of monomers? _____4_____ A typical protein polymer consists of hundreds of monomers in total, but these long molecules are composed of how many different kinds of monomers? _____20_____

b. Which part makes each of the four major kinds of nucleotides different from the other kinds? _____base_____ Which part makes each of the 20 major kinds of amino acids different from the other kinds? _____R-grp._____

---

a. 4; 20;   b. base; R group

64. Diagramed below are both the chemical formulas and simplified diagrams for several different amino acid monomers.

VALINE

GLUTAMIC ACID

LYSINE

PHENYLALANINE

a. Because all these molecules have the same amine (H_2N-) and carboxylic acid (-COOH) groups, they are called _____amino acids_____.

b. Attached to the top of the central carbon atom that joins the common amine and acid groups is a group that is different for each molecule diagramed. This different group is called the *R-grp* .

c. In the diagrams, the lines (———) represent which part of the amino acids? *amine* and *acid* Which part of the amino acid is represented by the variable geometric forms (△, ▢, etc.)? *R-grp*

d. Four different amino acids are shown on page 41. Approximately how many different kinds of amino acids are there? *20* By combining these amino acids in various sequences, protein molecules can be formed that contain roughly how many amino acids? *100's*

---

a. amino acids; b. R group; c. amine and acid, or carboxylic acid, groups; R-groups; d. about 20; hundreds (*Equivalent answer:* The idea is that proteins are long molecules that use a relatively few amino acids over and over in different sequences, just as DNA is a long molecule that uses only four nucleotides over and over in different sequences.)

65.

proline	pro
valine	*val*
glutamic acid	*glu*

Above are the names of three amino acids that we will encounter frequently in this book. Scientists often use a kind of shorthand to refer to amino acids, usually by using the first three letters of their chemical names. Complete the chart above by filling in the abbreviations for valine and glutamic acid.

---

val
glu

66. Below is a diagram of a hormone molecule, insulin.

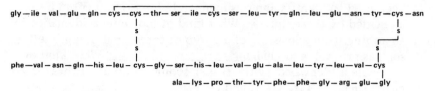

What kind of molecular units are indicated by ser, his, ala, gly, etc.? *amino acids* What kind of molecule is insulin, which is a polymer of such units? *protein*

---

amino acids; protein

67. In the same way that three small English letters represent amino acids, three of the base letters of DNA, a *triplet codon*, can be used to represent an amino acid.

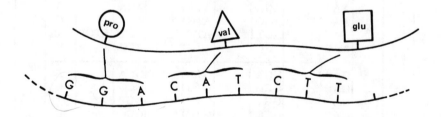

The diagram above suggests that, in the DNA for making sickle cell hemoglobin, the triplet codon name for proline is GGA. What is the triplet codon name for valine? _____CAT_____ ... for glutamic acid? _CTT_.

CAT; CTT

nucleo

68. Groups of three letters, such as JFK, LBJ, and FDR, have been used to identify famous men, and perhaps you could be identified by three initials. What kind of molecule is identified by an abbreviation consisting of a group of three small English letters, , such as pro, val, and glu? _amino acids_ What kind of molecule is identified by the triplet ~~codon~~ grouping of three DNA bases, such as GGA, CAT, and CTT? _amino acids._

---

amino acids (monomers of protein molecules) in both cases

69. When the four bases of DNA are combined in groups of three, 64 different triplet ~~codon~~s are possible, as indicated by the decoding chart below.

		Second Base				
		A	G	T	C	
First Base	A	AAA AAG } phe, AAT, AAC	AGA AGG AGT AGC } ser	ATA ATG } tyr, ATT ATC } STOP	ACA ACG } cys, ACT STOP, ACC try	A G T C	**Third Base**
	G	GAA } leu, GAG, GAT, GAC	GGA GGG GGT GGC } pro	GTA GTG } his, GTT GTC } gln	GCA GCG GCT GCC } arg	A G T C	
	T	TAA TAG } ile, TAT, TAC met; START	TGA TGG TGT TGC } thr	TTA TTG } asn, TTT TTC } lys	TCA TCG } ser, TCT TCC } arg	A G T C	
	C	CAA CAG CAT CAC } val START	CGA CGG CGT CGC } ala	CTA CTG } asp, CTT CTC } glu	CCA CCG CCT CCC } gly	A G T C	

44

a. According to the decoding chart, AAA is the triplet codon
    name for what amino acid (indicate its abbreviated name)?
    ___*phe*___ Is there a second triplet codon nearby that
    also identifies this amino acid? __*yes AAG*__ There can
    be more than one triplet codon name for an amino acid.
    Does a given codon ever specify more than one amino acid?
    ___*no*___

b. Most triplet codons name or specify amino acids, but five
    serve as punctuation, marking the beginning and end of a
    DNA segment. What do the codons ATT, ATC, and ACT
    stand for? __*STOP/end*__ Besides identifying amino acids,
    what do the codons TAC and CAC represent? __*beginning*__

c. What sequence of amino acids would be found in the protein
    produced by (or under the direction of) the DNA sequence
    GGACATCTT? __*pro val glu*__

---

a. phe; yes—AAG; no (Notice that there is never more than one
amino acid listed next to a codon. No confusion can arise from
anino acids having the same name.);   b. stop; start (i.e., stop or
start making a certain protein);   c. pro-val-glu

70. A triplet codon is a portion of DNA consisting of three
    ___*bases*___. A triplet codon specifies the placement
in a protein chain of one __*amino acid*__.

---

bases (or nucleotides, of which bases are the distinctive part);
amino acid

71. There are about 20 amino acids, but only four bases. One at
a time, bases could only code for four amino acids, and two at a
time (AA, AT, AG, AC, etc.) for only 16. How many bases are
actually used to code one amino acid? ___*3*___ What is
such a group of bases called? __*triplet codon*__

---

three (3); triplet codon

72. The DNA molecule for producing one complete protein is a *gene*. Since it takes a triplet ~~codon~~ of DNA to specify each amino acid in a protein, how many bases would be found in the gene for producing insulin, a protein formed initially by 84 amino acids? *3 X 84 = 252* An average protein consists of 500 amino acids, so how many bases must be found in the average gene? *1,500*

---

252 (3 x 84); 1,500 (3 x 500)

73. In the English language we have *letters* for spelling, *words* that name things, and *sentences* that express complete thoughts. In DNA language, what serve as:

a. letters for spelling hereditary information? *bases*
b. words for naming amino acids? *triplets*
c. sentences dictating the production of a particular protein?
    genes

---

a. bases (or GCAT, or nucleotides);   b. triplet codons (or groups of three bases);   c. genes

74. In the English language, we also have these three additional groupings of letters, words, and sentences:

> *paragraphs* . . . . groups of related sentences
> *pages* . . . . arbitrary groups of several sentences
> and paragraphs
> *book* . . . . a set of pages on some topic

Mark each of these groupings in DNA language as most like one of the English language groupings above:

page a. *chromosome*, a long, thread-like structure including many genes related to a variety of traits
paragraph b. *operon*, a small group of genes producing proteins related to the same general function

Book c.   *genome*, a complete set of chromosomes, containing DNA specifying all the hereditary traits of an organism

---

a. page;   b. paragraph;   c. book

75.   Below are two pictures: (A) a segment of DNA producing *operon* three proteins for utilizing milk sugar, and (B) DNA units for such fruit fly traits as eye color and body bristles. *chromosome*

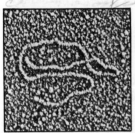 

Photograph of lac operon, Plate 5, p. 772 of *Nature*,   Photograph courtesy of Nov. 22, 1969. Courtesy of Dr. L. A. MacHattie.   Dr. Michael D. Parker.

From the descriptions given and your previous information, appropriately label these photographs as *chromosome* and *operon*.

A. operon;   B. chromosome

76.   base   operon   gene
        triplet codon   chromosome   genome

Match each DNA language component above with the appropriate description below and at the top of page 48:

Genome a.   a complete listing in DNA code of instructions for forming each and every trait of an organism
Base b.   one of the four letters used to write hereditary information in DNA code
Triplet c.   a group of DNA letters coding a particular amino acid
gene d.   a sequence of about 1,500 nucleotides producing one particular protein

47

operon e. a group of nine DNA segments producing nine proteins needed to make histidine

chromosome f. thread-like bodies in a cell's nucleus containing DNA for several different kinds of traits

---

a. genome; b. base; c. triplet codon; d. gene; e. operon; f. chromosome

77. In a language somewhat like English, DNA spells out heredi-tary information.
a. DNA language serves as the basis for hereditary trait develop-ment because it encodes information for forming *protein* molecules.
DNA language also serves as the basis for reproduction, because it carries information for forming additional _____*DNA*_____ molecules.
b. The sickle cell gene, for example, causes the formation of abnormally shaped red blood cells because it produces defec-tive _____*hemoglobin*_____ molecules. Sickle cell anemia is heredi-tary, because the abnormality is transmitted by _____*DNA*_____ molecules.

---

a. protein; DNA   b. hemoglobin (or protein, or sickle cell hemo-globin); DNA

78. The photograph of DNA at the beginning of this chapter showed DNA as a *double helix*, i.e., as two nucleotide polymers, or polynucleotides, spiralled around one another. The two strands, which may be called *gene* and *copy* strands, both function in DNA production, but only one strand of a double helix functions in protein pro-duction.

From your study of DNA language, would you expect protein to be produced by the gene strand or the copy strand? *gene*

---

gene strand

79. The sequence of bases along the gene strand of a DNA double helix stores information for producing proteins. If the sequence of bases in a DNA gene is changed, what sequence within proteins is also changed? *am ac.* Generally speaking, what else may be changed when the protein changes? *traits*

---

amino acid sequence; *Sample answer:* traits (or physical features, hereditary characteristics, etc.)

80. Changes in DNA base sequences which produce changes in proteins and hereditary traits are called *mutations*. Name a factor which causes such changes. *radiation* What aspect of science seeks to make alterations in DNA replication and function in the hope of correcting hereditary defects, etc.? _____

---

mutations; *Sample answer:* radiation (or certain chemicals); genetic engineering

81. Chemicals such as nitrogen mustard seem to cause chromo-somal damage. Are such chemicals a threat only to one individual or generation or to future generations? _____
Why? *future* _____

Sample answers: Possibly, future generations, if the chromosome damage is genetic (occurring in reproductive organs) rather than just somatic (occurring in other body cells). Chemical damage to

DNA in reproductive cells is hereditary because, to allow reproduction to occur, chromosomes in these cells are duplicated by the action of DNA producing more DNA. Mutated DNA will produce new DNA containing the same mutation.

Summary

The structure of DNA helps us to understand how DNA functions as a carrier of information for making both proteins and more DNA.

DNA is usually found in living cells as two very long strands coiled about each other to form a double helix. Each strand of DNA is a polymer, or chain, of repeated units called nucleotides. The sugar and phosphate groups of the nucleotides join in a line, and the four different bases of the nucleotides, designated as G, C, A, and T, protrude from this line much like letters set in a type holder. Typically, a sequence of about 1,500 of these base letters forms a gene, a DNA sentence coding the production of one particular kind of protein.

Proteins, also polymers, are long chains of amino acids joined as amine-acid strands with various sequences of 20 different R groups protruding along the chain. In protein synthesis, amino acids are lined up in an order specified by DNA. Three bases (a triplet codon) are needed to specify one amino acid.

DNA stores hereditary information somewhat in the same way that we store information in the English language. DNA's alphabet letters are its four *bases* (GCAT); its words are the *triplet codon* names for amino acids; its sentences are the *genes*. A gene consists of an average of 1,500 bases or 500 triplet codons specifying production of a particular protein. DNA's paragraphs are the *operons*, which are groups of genes producing proteins involved in the same function; its pages are the microscopically visible *chromosomes* containing genes for many traits; its book is the *genome*, a complete set of DNA instructions for developing a particular life form. The DNA language permits all the information for forming the thousands of individual human traits to be packed inside the nucleus of a tiny egg or sperm cell—a masterpiece of microminiature design.

B
T
G
O
C
G

50

Review Quiz

1. On the diagrams below, label a sugar, phosphate, base, nucleotide, amino acid, and R group.

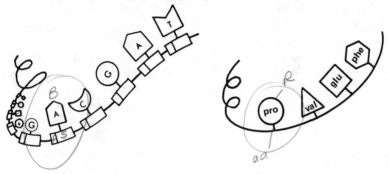

2. Because they are chains of repeated units, DNA and protein
molecules are both called <u>polymers</u>. The links or
monomers in DNA molecules are called <u>nucleotides</u> and
in proteins <u>amino acids</u>

   In structure, both DNA and protein molecules have backbones
made of two groups, with a third group protruding from the
side of the chain. Which groups make up the backbone of
DNA? <u>sugar-phos</u> . . . the backbone of a protein?
<u>amino-acid</u>

   What group protrudes from the side of a DNA chain?
<u>base</u> . . . from the side of a protein chain?
<u>R-grp.</u>

3. There are how many bases? <u>4</u> . . . amino acids? <u>20</u>

   How many bases are needed and used to code one amino acid?
<u>3</u>

   Since an average protein consists of about 500 amino acids in
total, approximately how many bases must there be in the
average DNA gene to make the average protein? <u>1500</u>

4. To compare DNA's language with English, match the following:

 _C_ (1) alphabet letter   a. a *gene* for producing
 _d_ (2) word   one protein
 _a_ (3) sentence   b. an *operon* or group of
 _b_ (4) paragraph   related genes
 _e_ (5) page   c. the four *bases*, GCAT
 _f_ (6) book   d. the *triplet ~~codon~~* name
                                    for an amino acid
                                 e. a *chromosome* with
                                  hundreds or thousands
                                  of DNA genes
                                 f. a *genome* with a com-
                                  plete set of genes deter-
                                  mining an individual's
                                  hereditary traits

5. Match each element of DNA language below with its description:

 _f_ (1) base   a. DNA code for a com-
 _e_ (2) triplet ~~codon~~   plete set of an individ-
 _d_ (3) gene   ual's hereditary traits
 _c_ (4) operon   b. a microscopically visible
 _b_ (5) chromosome   thread-like structure
 _a_ (6) genome   including many DNA
                                  genes
                                  c. group of DNA genes
                                  producing proteins re-
                                  lated to the same func-
                                  tion
                                  d. an average of 1,500
                                  bases producing one
                                  particular kind of
                                  protein
                                  e. group of three bases
                                  specifying one particu-
                                  lar amino acid
                                  f. G, C, A, or T

6.

		Second Base				
		A	G	T	C	
F i r s t B a s e	A	AAA AAG } phe AAT AAC	AGA AGG AGT AGC } ser	ATA ATG } tyr ATT ATC } STOP	ACA ACG } cys ACT STOP ACC try	A G T C	T h i r d B a s e
	G	GAA GAG GAT GAC } leu	GGA GGG GGT GGC } pro	GTA GTG } his GTT GTC } gln	GCA GCG GCT GCC } arg	A G T C	
	T	TAA TAG } ile TAT TAC met; START	TGA TGG TGT TGC } thr	TTA TTG } asn TTT TTC } lys	TCA TCG } ser TCT TCC } arg	A G T C	
	C	CAA CAG CAT CAC } val START	CGA CGG CGT CGC } ala	CTA CTG } asp CTT CTC } glu	CCA CCG CCT CCC } gly	A G T C	

On the basis of the decoding chart above,

a. What amino acid has the DNA triplet codon name GGA?
    ___pro___ ... CAT? ___val___ ... CTT?
    ___glu___

b. What sequence of amino acids would be produced by
    the DNA sequence GGACTTCTT? _pro glu glu_ ...
    by GGACATCTT? _pro val glu_

c. What effect does the difference between these two DNA
    base sequences have on the shape of red blood cells?

    ① normal hgb.

    ② sickle cell hgb

7. Persons whose red blood cell hemoglobin proteins contain the amino acid sequence pro-val-glu suffer from sickle cell anemia, whereas persons whose corresponding sequence is pro-glu-glu do not. The normal hemoglobin is produced by the base sequence GGACTTCTT and the sickle cell hemoglobin by the different base sequence GGACATCTT.

    a. What general name is given to changes in the DNA base sequence that produce changes in proteins and changes in the traits related to those proteins? *mutations*

    b. Name one agent which can cause a change in DNA. *chem.*

    c. Can such changes in DNA be passed on to future generations? *yes*

    d. What branch of science is working to discover ways to alter DNA? *gen. eng.*

Check your answers against those on page 144.

54

III
DNA: REPLICATION, REPAIR, AND REPRODUCTION

Introduction

"Like begets like." The ability of life forms to reproduce is the most well-known characteristic distinguishing living from nonliving things. This ability to reproduce is based on the replication of DNA molecules, which encode information for forming all of an organism's proteins and hereditary traits. DNA in a single cell is copied, and the cell then divides into two cells, each having one copy of all of the original DNA. Sexually reproducing forms pass their traits, coded by DNA, through egg and sperm cells.

Alterations, called mutations, sometimes occur in the copying of DNA's hereditary information. Since such mutations can be harmful to future generations, it is fortunate indeed that cells have the means to repair many of the mutations in DNA. This repair process has also attracted the attention of geneticists seeking to correct hereditary defects.

Upon completing this chapter, you should be able to:

- describe DNA replication, the basis of all reproduction, in terms of the interlocking of DNA bases.

- identify several factors involved in DNA replication, and explain why DNA is not truly self-reproducing.

- relate the replication of DNA to chromosome structure and reproduction and the life cycle of a cell.

- comment on the repair of mutated DNA, both by natural processes and by scientists.

82.　Reproduction begins when the chromosomes bearing an organism's genetic instructions replicate or reproduce themselves. Most viruses and bacterial cells have a single, loop-shaped chromosome that replicates by forming a second loop:

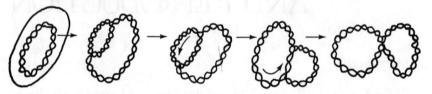

What kind of molecules form this loop-shaped chromosome?
___DNA___

DNA

83.　Unlike the simple loops of viruses and bacteria, chromosomes of plants, animals, and human beings are complex rods or threads that replicate by forming a daughter chromosome that remains attached for a while to its parent chromosome:

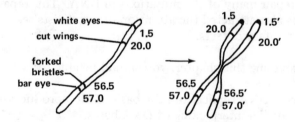

If the gene for forked bristles is found at position 56.5 on the parent chromosome, what gene will be found at position 56.5' on the daughter chromosome? ___forked bristles___ Although chromosomes are about half protein and half DNA, which molecule carries the hereditary information? ___DNA___

Sample answer: a copy of the gene for forked bristles;　DNA

84.

As the diagrams above suggest, whether a chromosome is a loop or a long, complex thread, the molecule bearing its hereditary instructions is DNA. How many polymer strands of DNA make up the coiled strand that is the basic structural element of each chromosome? _____*2*_____ What shape is formed by the coiling of these strands about each other? _____*double helix*_____

---

two; double helix

85. Using the x-ray diffraction photographs of Wilkins (plus some cardboard cutouts and their own insight), Watson and Crick deduced that DNA is a double helix consisting of two coiled polynucleotide strands joined by the interlocking pairing of their bases.

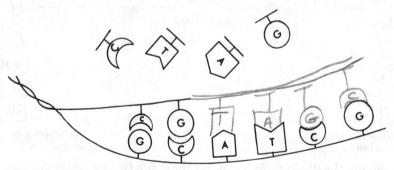

Complete the diagram of a DNA double helix above by pairing the bases of the free or unattached nucleotides.

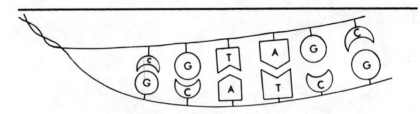

86. Watson and Crick theorized that DNA reproduces by unzipping and then rezipping, as partially diagramed below.

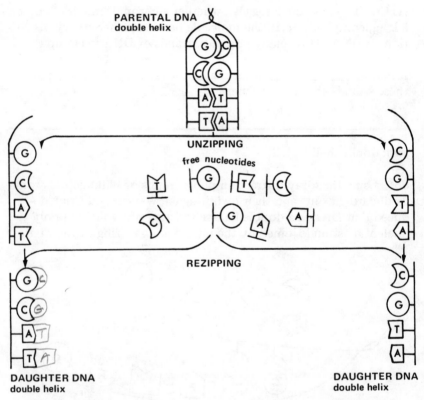

Complete the diagram above by finishing the two daughter double helices that would be formed by rezipping with the free nucleotides that are continually synthesized within the cell.

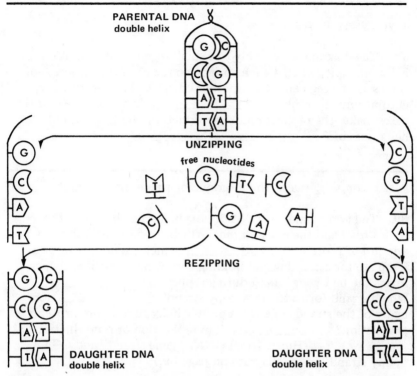

PARENTAL DNA
double helix

UNZIPPING

free nucleotides

REZIPPING

DAUGHTER DNA
double helix

DAUGHTER DNA
double helix

87. Use the completed diagram above to answer the following questions about DNA replication.

a. Are the two daughter helices produced by replication identical to each other; that is, do they have the same series of base pairs? ___yes___ Is each identical to the single parental DNA double helix? ___yes___

b. Suppose the base sequence in the left strand of the parental helix GCAT were part of the gene for forming the protein responsible for curly hair. Do both daughter double helices contain the GCAT gene strand sequence? ___yes___ When the daughter DNA helices are divided between two cells during reproduction of cells in the scalp, would both daughter cells be able to produce the protein for curly hair?

___yes___

a. yes; yes;   b. yes; yes

88. The diagram shows only one small segment of a DNA double helix unzipping so that each strand can rezip. If this process continues as one segment after another unzips and rezips, can a whole chromosome be replicated? __*yes*__ What property of the bases makes the replication or reproduction of a DNA double helix possible? __*interlocking bases*__

yes;   *Sample answer:* the interlocking shapes of the bases

89. The two strands of DNA double helix may be called the *gene strand* and the *copy strand*. Which strand directs the production of proteins? __*gene*__ Which strand, acting as a template for attracting and holding complementary base shapes, forms the new gene strand during replication? __*copy*__ Which strand forms the new copy strand? __*gene*__ How many of the strands in a DNA double helix function in protein production? __*1*__ . . . in replication or reproduction? __*2*__ (Hint: Label GCAT "gene strand" and CGTA "copy strand" in the diagram on page 59.)

gene strand; copy strand; gene strand; one; two

90. (G)   [A]   (C)   [T]

The interlocking pairing of bases is the key to the replication of DNA and, hence, to the reproduction of all life.

a.   According to the shapes we have used to represent the bases, what base pairs with G? __*C*__ . . . with A? __*T*__ Are any other base pairs possible? __*no*__

b.   At the top of the next page, diagram the two kinds of base pairs made possible by the complementary or interlocking shapes of DNA bases.

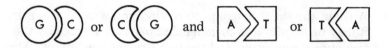

a. C; T; *no* other pairs are possible;   b. in any orientation:

and   or

91. The formation of G-C and A-T base pairs involves *hydrogen bonds*, the attraction of relatively negative O (oxygen) and N (nitrogen) atoms for a relatively positive H (hydrogen) atom held between them.

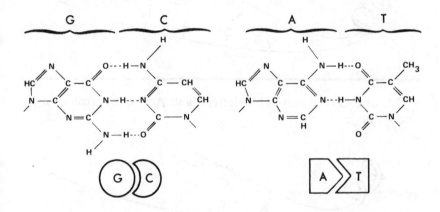

a.   How many hydrogen bonds, indicated by dotted lines, are shown in the structural formulas above between G and C? ____3____ . . . between A and T? ____2____

b.   Although a hydrogen bond is the physical force holding a base pair together, our simplified diagrams suggest that the ability of the bases to form hydrogen bonds depends upon what property? _interlocking shapes of bases_

61

a. three; two (Incidentally, the presence of three hydrogen bonds in G-C pairs and only two in A-T pairs makes G-C bonds harder to break or "melt," and this difference is of some experimental value.); b. *Sample answer:* the interlocking shapes of the bases

92.   It is convenient to represent DNA with lines for the sugar-phosphate backbones and letters for the bases.

a.   Without the shape diagrams to remind you which bases pair, it may be helpful to remember that pairs are formed by the two *curved* line letters and the two *straight* line letters. What, then, are the two kinds of DNA base pairs? __C G__ and __A T__

b.   Complete the base pairing in the helix diagramed below.

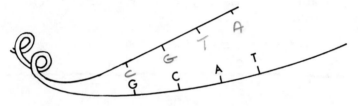

a. G-C or C-G (the curved line letters) and A-T or T-A (the straight line letters);
b.

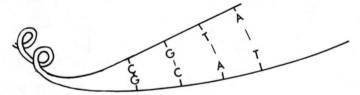

93.   The gene for producing sickle cell hemoglobin includes the base sequence GGACAT. At the top of the next page, diagram the short section of DNA (without the coiling) that would be formed by the base pairing of the gene strand segment (GGACAT) and its copy strand.

G	C
G	C
A	T
C	G
A	T
T	A

Sample answer (any orientation is acceptable):

```
─ G ─ C ─
─ G ─ C ─
─ A ─ T ─
─ C ─ G ─
─ A ─ T ─
─ T ─ A ─
```

94. Now, trace the reproduction of the DNA helix containing a segment of the sickle cell gene by completing the following:

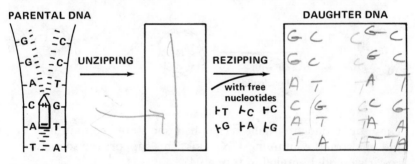

PARENTAL DNA

```
─ G ┆ ┆ C ─
─ G ┆ ┆ C ─
─ A ┆ ┆ T ─
─ C ┆ ┆ G ─
─ A ┆ ┆ T ─
─ T ┆ ┆ A ─
```

UNZIPPING → REZIPPING →

with free nucleotides
⊦T ⊦C ⊦C
⊦G ⊦A ⊦G

DAUGHTER DNA

G	C	C	G	C
G	C		G	C
A	T		A	T
C	G		C	G
A	T		A	A
T	A		T	A

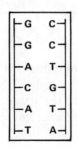

```
─ G    C ─
─ G    C ─
─ A    T ─
─ C    G ─
─ A    T ─
─ T    A ─
```

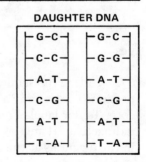

DAUGHTER DNA

```
─ G-C ─   ─ G-C ─
─ C-C ─   ─ G-G ─
─ A-T ─   ─ A-T ─
─ C-G ─   ─ C-G ─
─ A-T ─   ─ A-T ─
─ T-A ─   ─ T-A ─
```

95. The replication shown in frame 94 is one small section of a base paired gene strand. Would continued unzipping and rezipping of segments along the helix produce two copies of the whole gene? _____yes_____ . . . of the next gene in the series along the chromosome? _____yes_____ . . . of the whole chromosome? _____yes_____ . . . of other chromosomes, making possible production of two complete sets of DNA-encoded traits? _____yes_____

---

yes; yes; yes; yes

96. DNA replication as shown in frame 94 is called *semiconservative* because each daughter helix contains one of the original (conserved) strands and one new strand formed of polymerized free nucleotides. To test this model, Meselson and Stahl labeled one strand of a bacterial chromosome with heavy ^{15}N and let it replicate with light ^{14}N labeled nucleotides.

They found daughter helices each had one strand containing ^{15}N and one strand containing ^{14}N. Does this support the semiconservative model implied in frame 94? _____yes_____

---

yes

97. Testing the semiconservative model with a larger chromosome presumed to contain a single, supercoiled DNA double helix as its core, Taylor labeled *one strand* of the parental double helix with radioactive ^{3}H and let it replicate with nonradioactive H, as shown in the diagrams at the top of the next page.

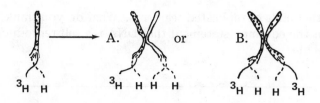

Base - pairing

The grains or dots represent ^3H. Would you predict that Taylor
obtained result A or result B? ___*A*___

A. For explanation, study this diagram:

UNZIP → REZIP with H →

^3HH H H
only one strand
with radioactive ^3H label

98. The experiments cited above and many others support the
Watson-Crick-Wilkens semiconservative model implied in your
diagram of DNA replication. According to this model, reproduction of genetic information, the basis of reproduction in all life
forms, depends upon what simple property of DNA bases?

*complementary bases which
form G-C   A-T*

Sample answer: their interlocking or complementary shapes,
which enable them to form the base pairs G-C and A-T

99. Base pairing is certainly the key to DNA replication, but it
is not the only factor. For replication, DNA also requires: (1) an
abundant supply of free *nucleotides* manufactured from food
substances, (2) an *energy* supply to zip together new sugar-phosphate backbones, and (3) several specialized *enzymes* for such
roles as unzipping the helix, adding bases in order, and tying

65

together ends of replicated segments. What do you think, then, about the common statement that DNA is a self-reproducing molecule?

although DNA can be replic. - is not totally independent needs outside factors

---

Sample answer: DNA is *not* truly self-reproducing. DNA contains information for directing its own reproduction, but its actual replication requires a host of outside factors.

100. Among the factors DNA requires for its replication are the following:

        (1) free nucleotides
        (2) energy source
        (3) enzymes

If DNA replication is compared to a construction job, which of the three above is the raw material supply? ____1____ . . . the power supply? ____2____ . . . the workman for putting the parts together correctly? ____3____

---

(1) free nucleotides (continually manufactured from food taken in by living cells); (2) energy source (which actually consists of two extra phosphates attached to each nucleotide*); (3) enzymes

*NOTE: It is interesting that nucleotides serve not only as the building blocks of the nucleic acid molecules involved in heredity, but also in tri-phosphate forms, such as ATP and GTP, which act as the cell's chief distributors of chemical energy.

66

see p. 72   #9   145

101. The role of raw materials and energy in DNA replication is clear. Let us examine now the role of enzymes. Enzymes are large protein molecules with active sites in their surfaces which enable them to act on molecules with complementary shapes. Which of the molecular shapes below could be acted upon by the enzyme diagramed? _____*B*_____ and _____*C*_____

B and C

102. Enzymes usually act either to combine small molecules or to break apart large molecules. Depending upon conditions, they may promote either the formation or the breaking down of the same molecule.

a.   Which enzyme below, A or B, would act to digest (break down) the molecule of table sugar, sucrose? _____*B*_____

b.   Would the enzyme you named above also have the proper shape to combine the ◯ (glucose) and △ (fructose) subunits of sucrose under proper conditions? _____*yes*_____

a. B;   b. yes

103. Enzymes are often named by adding *-ase* to the name of the molecule they affect. For example, the enzyme that digests lactose (milk sugar) is called lactase. What, then, is the likely name for the enzyme affecting sucrose (table sugar)? _____*sucrase*_____

104. There are three kinds of enzymes involved in DNA replication:

(1) *nucleases*—function in unzipping by nicking or digesting openings in sugar-phosphate backbones so base pairs can separate;
(2) *polymerases*—function in rezipping by joining sugar and phosphate units of free nucleotides as they pair with bases into positions opened up by nucleases;
(3) *ligases*—tie together segments of replicated DNA produced by nuclease and polymerase activity.

Using these verbal descriptions, associate each process diagramed below with either nuclease, polymerase, or ligase activity.

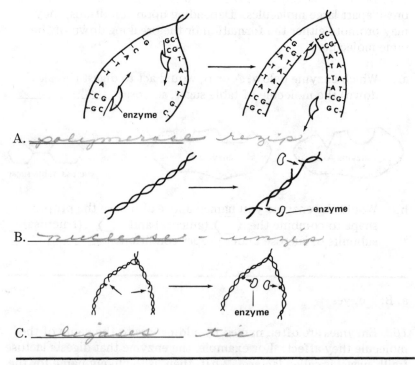

A. *polymerase* *rezip*

B. *nuclease* *unzip*

C. *ligases* *tie*

A. polymerase; B. nuclease; C. ligase

105. Match each enzyme with its function in DNA replication.

_B_(1) nuclease   a. zips together new DNA
_A_(2) polymerase   strands by joining sugar and
_C_(3) ligase   phosphate groups
                            b. unzips DNA helices by mak-
                                ing openings in the sugar-
                                phosphate backbones
                            c. unites loose ends of replicated
                                DNA segments

---

(1) b;   (2) a;   (3) c

106. Each of the three kinds of replication enzymes involved in
DNA replication has a name suggesting its function.

a. Chains of repeated molecular units are called polymers, so
    the enzyme that zips together free nucleotides to form
    polymers is called a _polymerase_.
b. The word *ligate* means tie, so the enzyme that ties together
    replicated DNA segments is called a _ligase_.
c. Enzymes that digest proteins are called proteases and
    enzymes that digest lipids are lipases. Thus, the enzyme that
    breaks down nucleic acids, such as DNA, is called a
    nuclease.

---

a. polymerase;   b. ligase;   c. nuclease

107. We have just discussed three enzymes that are involved in
DNA replication. The replication process involves: (1) the diges-
tion of the sugar-phosphate backbones to unzip DNA helices,
(2) the joining together of new sugar and phosphate groups to zip
together new DNA strands, and (3) the binding of loose ends of
replicated DNA segments. Write the enzyme involved in each step.

(1)_nuclease_(2)_polymerase_(3) _ligase_

(1) nuclease; (2) polymerase; (3) ligase

108. Enzymes like those just described function in the replication of
DNA *and also* in the repair of damaged or mutated DNA. Below
is a section of DNA damaged by ultraviolet light. This has caused
adjacent T's to break away from A's and cross link instead to themselves to form "thymine (T) dimers."

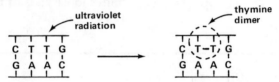

What are such radiation-caused changes in DNA called?
mutations What is the hereditary signficance of such
changes?

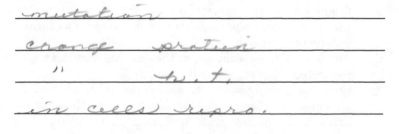

mutations; *Sample answer:* Mutations in DNA can cause changes
in the proteins made by DNA and, consequently, changes in
hereditary traits. Mutations in DNA are passed on to later cell
generations when DNA replicates, thus passing on the hereditary
defect, either to other body cells (somatic mutation) or to another
generation (if the mutation is genetic, and occurs in reproductive
cells).

109. Each of the three kinds of enzymes for DNA replication is
involved in one of the three steps in DNA repair, as shown at the
top of the next page.

a.

The first step in DNA repair is removing the damaged segment. Which kind of enzyme performs this function—ligase, polymerase, or nuclease? *nuclease*

b.

The second step is splicing in a new base-pair segment. Which enzyme functions here? *polymerase*

c.

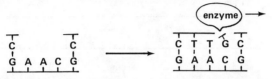

The third and final step is uniting the new, spliced-in segment with the rest of the helix. What enzyme does this?

ligase

---

a. nuclease;   b. polymerase;   c. ligase

110. Three steps and three enzymes are involved in both the replication and the repair of segments of DNA. Mark the steps below from 1 (first) to 3 (last).

__2__a. polymerase zips together the sugar-phosphate backbones of nucleotides

__1__b. nuclease causes openings in the DNA backbone, enabling base pairs to unzip

__3__c. ligase ties the replicated or repaired segment of DNA into the rest of the helix

---

a. 2;   b. 1;   c. 3

111. DNA repair is a most remarkable process. What science, the aim of which is the correction of hereditary defects, would involve studies of DNA repair? _____ If scientists learn how to control the DNA repair process, what kinds of things might they do?

genetic engineering
— elim h. defects

---

genetic engineering; *Sample answer:* Control of DNA repair might mean the correction and elimination of many hereditary diseases, such as sickle cell anemia, albinism, galactosemia, etc. On the other hand, the ability to splice in DNA segments could result in attempts to control human heredity, with potentially undesirable or uncontrollable results.

112. A major initial step toward the control of DNA was achieved by Kornberg and his colleagues. They extracted a loop of DNA from a virus and induced it to replicate in culture. What raw materials must they have added to the DNA? *free nucs* What enzymes would they have utilized? *nuclease, polymerase, ligase*

Sample answer: free nucleotides (which were actually added in energized form as triphosphates); nucleases, polymerases, and ligases

113. With the factors listed in frame 112, plus several others added to a test tube containing no living material, Kornberg and his colleagues got the extracted DNA loops to make several copies of themselves.

a.   Do these experiments suggest DNA is totally self-reproducing? ___*no*___

b.   Do these experiments qualify as "creating life in a test tube"? ___*no*___

c.   Of what potential value are these experiments to the geneticist?

___*research*_____

_____

---

a. no (DNA carries information for directing its own reproduction, but its replication requires many factors normally produced only by living cells, such as an abundance of energized nucleotides and several complex enzymes, which in this instance were furnished by the experimenters.);   b. no (Although several news accounts called the experiments "creating life in a test tube," Kornberg and his colleagues noted that they were simply using enzymes and other factors to induce natural DNA to act outside a living cell as it normally does within a living cell.)   c. *Sample answer:* Any of several things may have occurred to you: The technique could be used for mass producing corrected DNA for insertion into genes, for producing DNA resistant to bacteria or cancers, or simply as a research system for learning more about DNA.

---

114. The work of Watson, Crick, Kornberg, and many others has revealed much about the replication of DNA, which is the basis of all reproduction. But many details are still not clearly understood:

(1)   The two strands of a double helix are antiparallel, with one running sugar to phosphate (called $3' \rightarrow 5'$) and the other phosphate to sugar ($5' \rightarrow 3'$). Known polymerases work only $5' \rightarrow 3'$, meaning the two strands must somehow be replicated in opposite directions.

(2)   How do nucleases know where to split up the sugar phosphate backbone for either replication or repair, and what triggers the start of DNA replication?

(3)

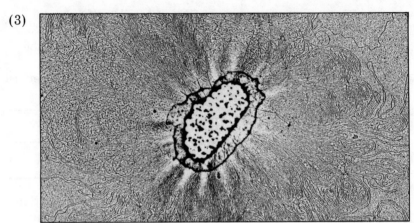

Photograph courtesy of Dr. L. A. MacHattie.

Above is a photograph of a supercoiled DNA loop extruded from a ruptured bacterium. How can such an incredibly long, highly packed loop of DNA be replicated in about half an hour, with less than 1 mistake per ten million replications of a gene?

Despite these uncertainties and many others, it seems certain that the reproductive ability of DNA is based on one very simple feature of its structure. What structural feature is that?

interlocking bases

Sample answer: interlocking pairing of DNA bases

115. It is remarkable indeed that the complex process of DNA reproduction depends upon the simple process of base pairing.

a. What simple feature of DNA bases makes their pairing possible? _complementary shapes_

b. What two kinds of base pairs are possible? _A T_ and _G C_

c. A reproductive unit of DNA includes two strands. What holds these two strands together? _H-bonds_ What shape is formed by the intertwining of these two strands? _double helix_

a. *Sample answer:* interlocking or complementary shapes;   b. G-C (or C-G) and A-T (or T-A) (either order);   c. base pairing or hydrogen bonds; double helix

116. The concept of base pairing you have mastered should serve you well in understanding the process by which DNA replicates and repairs itself, as well as the process by which DNA makes protein, to be described next.

117. Diagramed below are the chemical structures of the DNA bases with their names.

GUANINE   CYTOSINE   ADENINE   THYMINE

DNA bases are either *pyrimidines*, with *one* six-sided ring of atoms, or *purines*, with *two* rings, a six-sided ring sharing one side with a five-sided ring.

a.   Which of the DNA bases—guanine, cytosine, adenine, or thymine—are purines? (spell out the names) _adenine_ and _guanine_ Which two are pyrimidines? _thymine_ and _cytosine_

b.   The word pyrimidine contains the letter y. Does the chemical name of each pyrimidine base also contain the letter y? _yes_

a. guanine and adenine (purines, either order); cytosine and thymine (pyrimidines, either order);   b. yes (P̲y̲rimidine, cy̲tosine, and thy̲mine all contain y's, a useful memory aid.)

118.

guan-
aden-
cyto-   -ine (pronounced "-een")
thym-

The names for the four DNA bases all end in -ine. From the prefixes above, put together the names of the two pyrimidine bases. *cytosine* and *thymine* . . . the two purine bases. *adenine* and *guanine*

---

cytosine and thymine;   guanine and adenine

119. We have been using the letters G, C, A, and T to represent the bases of DNA. What are the chemical names these letters represent?

G –

G: guanine, C: cytosine, A: adenine, T: thymine (any order)

120. Diagramed below are the two kinds of pairs formed by DNA bases, with the hydrogen bonds joining them indicated by dotted lines.

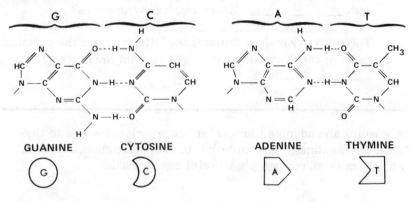

a. Do purines or pyrimidines consist of a structure with two rings, like this? *purines*

Which has one ring, like this? *pyrimidines*

b. In the base pairs above, a purine is always paired to a (purine/pyrimidine) *pyr* and a pyrimidine is always paired to a *pur*. How many ring structures are there in a base pair combination? *3* The distance between the strands in a DNA double helix (is always the same/varies from place to place) *same*.

---

a. purine; pyrimidine; b. pyrimidine, purine; three; is always the same (In fact, without the regularity of purine-pyrimidine pairing, a double helix structure would be impossible.)

121. A DNA base pair is formed by one base with a double ring and one base with a single ring.

a. The bases consisting of single rings are called *pyr*. The two bases of this kind are C and T, whose chemical names are *cytosine* and *thymine*
b. The bases consisting of double rings are called *purines* The two bases of this kind are G and A, whose chemical names are *guanine* and *adenine*
c. What is the general significance of this base pairing? _____

same diameter → double helix -

---

a. pyrimidines; cytosine and thymine; b. purines; guanine and adenine; c. *Sample answer:* Such base pairs make possible the double helix structure of DNA and its reproduction and repair.

Summary

The replication of DNA depends on the fact that the bases of DNA are shaped to interlock, A with T and G with C (adenine-thymine and guanine-cytosine). During reproduction, a DNA double helix unzips and each of the two strands then rezips, with nucleotides being locked into place by paired bases. By this means, both the single, naked, loop-shaped chromosomes of bacteria and viruses and the multiple, protein-complexed, thread-like chromosomes of plants, animals, and human beings are duplicated. The duplicated chromosomes with their hereditary information are then passed from one cell to the next during cell division or as egg and sperm cells are formed and unite.

Although it is the basis of reproduction, DNA is not truly self-reproducing. Its replication requires energy, new nucleotides, and a group of three enzymes to unzip and rezip the double helix properly. Three kinds of enzymes—nuclease, polymerase, and ligase—also serve in DNA repair, a fascinating process by which mutated or damaged sections of DNA are cut out and the correct base sequence is spliced in. Geneticists may one day be able to control these processes, and thereby control the reproductive pattern of an organism or correct its hereditary defects.

Review Quiz

1. Diagram the four bases of DNA, showing how they interlock to form two kinds of pairs.

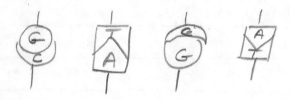

2. What is the chief significance of DNA base pairing?

   interlocking base pairing basis

3. The two strands of a DNA double helix may be called the gene strand and the copy strand. Which strand or strands make protein molecules? *gene* Which strand(s) make DNA during replication? *gene & copy*

4. Diagram the unzipping and rezipping process by which this portion of a DNA double helix would replicate itself:

5. Where do the fresh nucleotides for base pairing come from? *food* Unzipping and rezipping also require energy, as well as the assistance of large proteins with slots or active sites on their surfaces that enable them to break apart or combine other molecules. What are these proteins called?

   enzymes

6. Is DNA a self-reproducing molecule? Explain your answer.

   no - needs food (free nucs)
   + enzymes
   But can produce
   copy of itself

7. The kinds of enzymes involved in DNA replication also function in the repair of damaged or mutated DNA.

   a. Which enzyme removes the damaged or mutated section of DNA—nuclease, ligase, or polymerase?
   nuc Which enzyme zips together the new nucleotides as they base pair into position? *poly*
   Which enzyme ties the new strand into the original DNA? *lig*
   b. What is the significance of DNA repair?

   1) - genetic eng.
   * - prev - her. defects*

   2) elim. mutations

8. Are bacteria and viruses characterized by a chromosome which is thread-like and complexed with protein, or a naked loop of DNA? *naked DNA* What is the basic structure of chromosomes in the cells of plants, animals, and human beings? *thread-like*
   protein

9. Can DNA appropriately be called the "key to life"? Explain your answer.

_____

_____

_____

_____

_____

_____

10. The following questions concern some of the terminology associated with DNA bases.

   a. Which of the four DNA bases—guanine, cytosine, adenine, or thymine—are single ring pyrimidines like this? N⬡ _____*C*_____ and _____*T*_____ Which

   are double ring purines like this? N⬡N _____*A*_____

   and _____*G*_____

   b. Is a base pair formed as a purine-purine, pyrimidine-pyrimidine, or purine-pyrimidine combination?
   _____✓_____

   c. What are the chemical names indicated by the initials G, C, A, and T? *guanine* , *adenine*, *cytosine* and *thymine*

Check your answers against those on pages 144 and 145.

IV
PROTEIN SYNTHESIS: RNA'S ROLE

Introduction

In the last chapter, we considered DNA replication, the process by which hereditary information is copied and made available for future generations. In this chapter we examine the process by which DNA directs the synthesis of the protein molecules that are directly responsible for producing particular hereditary traits.

As mentioned earlier, DNA acts indirectly in protein systhesis. DNA actually produces a related nucleic acid, RNA (*ribo*nucleic *a*cid). The series of bases (triplet codons) of RNA determines the series of amino acid R groups along a protein molecule. For the protein synthesis process, enzymes and phosphate molecules for energy are also required.

This chapter focuses on the role of RNA molecules. Upon completing the chapter, you should be able to:

- describe how RNA differs from its related nucleic acid, DNA.

- describe the basic structure and function of the three kinds of RNA participating in protein synthesis: ribosomal RNA, messenger RNA, and transfer RNA (rRNA, mRNA, and tRNA).

- explain the role of base pairing in RNA function.

- indicate the effect of antibiotics on RNA function.

122. DNA is involved in two vital processes:

(1) *replication*—the reproduction of double helices which store hereditary information, and
(2) *protein synthesis*—the production of protein molecules responsible for particular hereditary traits.

In which process does a series of DNA bases regulate the order of a series of amino acids?___*2*___
In which process does a series of DNA bases regulate the order of another series of bases?___*1*___

---

protein synthesis; replication

123. Before it can produce either proteins or additional DNA, a segment of DNA must be unzipped or opened:

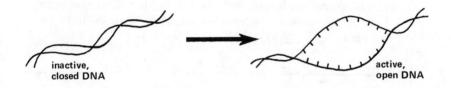

inactive,
closed DNA

active,
open DNA

Are one or both strands of an open segment active in DNA replication? (one/both) ___*both*___
Are one or both strands of an open segment active in protein synthesis? ___*one*___

---

both; one (the gene strand)

124. The diagram at the top of the next page shows a portion of the DNA gene strand directing the production of sickle cell hemoglobin. We will use it to review the basic plan of protein synthesis.

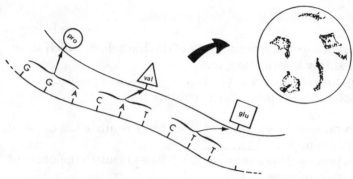

a. Both DNA and proteins are polymers, or chains of repeated
    molecular units. Which one is a polymer of amino acids?
    protein.. of nucleotides? _DNA_

b. According to the diagram, how many bases are used to direct
    the placement of one amino acid in a polymer chain?
    _3_ What is such a group of bases called?
    triplet What name is given to the base series used to
    produce an entire protein, such as sickle cell hemoglobin?

    gene

c. If 574 amino acids were included in sickle cell hemoglobin,
    how many bases or nucleotides would be involved in its pro-
    duction? _574 X 3 = 1722_

---

a. protein; DNA;   b. three; triplet ~~codon~~; gene;   c. 1,722 (3 x
574)

125. Use the DNA-protein chart at the top of the next page to
answer the following questions.

a. According to the DNA-protein chart, what amino acid (using
    abbreviated names) is specified by the triplet ~~codon~~ GGA?
    pro ...CAT? _val_ ...CTT?
    glu What amino acid sequence would be pro-
    duced by the DNA base sequence GGACATCTT?
    proval glu

b. If the second A in the sequence above (GGACATCTT) were
    changed to T, would the amino acid sequence produced by

84

		Second Base					
		A	G	T	C		
F i r s t B a s e	A	AAA AAG phe AAT AAC	AGA AGG AGT AGC ser	ATA ATG tyr ATT ATC STOP	ACA ACG cys ACT STOP ACC try	A G T C	T h i r d B a s e
	G	GAA GAG leu GAT GAC	GGA GGG GGT GGC pro	GTA GTG his GTT GTC gln	GCA GCG GCT arg GCC	A G T C	
	T	TAA TAG ile TAT TAC met; START	TGA TGG TGT thr TGC	TTA TTG asn TTT TTC lys	TCA TCG ser TCT TCC arg	A G T C	
	C	CAA CAG CAT val CAC START	CGA CGG CGT ala CGC	CTA CTG asp CTT CTC glu	CCA CCG CCT gly CCC	A G T C	

the changed DNA also change? ___yes___ What are
such changes in DNA base sequences called? ___mutations___
What is their effect on hereditary traits? ___changes___
___passed on change pro___

a. pro; val; glu; pro-val-glu (part of the sequence in sickle cell
hemoglobin);   b. yes (The sequence would become that of normal
hemoglobin.); mutations; *Sample answer:* Mutations, or changes
in DNA, can produce changes in proteins and traits.

126. In practice, the protein synthesis process involves RNA
molecules. The molecular structure of RNA is compared with that
of DNA on the next page.

DNA   RNA

a. As suggested by the diagrams, which nucleic acid (NA) is
    normally single stranded? ___R or A___ Which is normally
    a double helix? ___DN A___
b. The four bases of DNA are GCAT. What takes the place of
    T in RNA? ___U___ Does the shape diagramed for
    this base suggest it would pair with A as T does? ___yes___
    In DNA, base pairs G-C and A-T are possible. What two kinds
    of base pairs are possible between RNA molecules?
    ___G C___ and ___A-U___.

---

a. RNA; DNA;   b. U (which stands for uracil); yes (U is missing a
small side group present in T, but the group is not in a position to
affect pairing.); G-C and A-U

127. Protein assembly takes place in the cell cytoplasm at the site
of complex particles called ribosomes. DNA is located in the cell
nucleus.

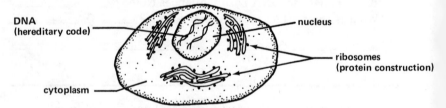

DNA
(hereditary code)   nucleus

                                                     ribosomes
                                                     (protein construction)

cytoplasm

If only because of its physical separation from ribosomes, DNA
would need a "go-between" molecule to direct protein synthesis.

What kind of nucleic acid molecule serves this go-between function? Give its initials, then spell out its name. ___R n A___

RNA;
ribonucleic acid

128. RNA differs from DNA in (1) normally occurring as single
strands, and (2) having U (uracil) instead of T (thymine) as the
base that pairs with A. A third difference between the two kinds
of nucleic acids is revealed by a close-up look at the atomic structure of the sugars making up the sugar portions of their nucleotides.

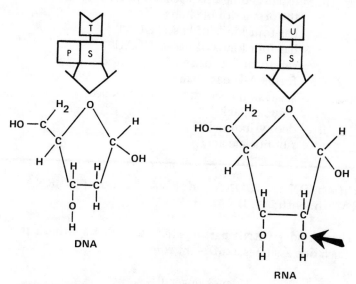

a.   One of the sugars above is *ribose,* and the other is *deoxyribose*
(*deoxy-* indicates the lack of an oxygen atom, O). Which of
these sugars is found in DNA? _deoxy_ ... in RNA?
ribose

b.   Since nucleotide polymers were first found most prominently
in the cell's nucleus, DNA and RNA are both called *nucleic
acids.* As a result of differences in their sugars, which is
properly called ribonucleic acid? _RNA_ ... deoxyribonucleic acid? _DNA_ What does the R stand
for in RNA? _ribose_ ... the D in DNA?
deoxyribose the NA in both names? _nucleic acid_

a. deoxyribose; ribose;   b. RNA; DNA; ribose or ribo-; deoxyribose or deoxyribo-; nucleic acid

129. Major similarities and minor differences characterize the two
kinds of nucleic acids, DNA and RNA. Mark the following as
descriptive of *DNA, RNA,* or *both.*

both	a.	polymer or nucleotides
DNA	b.	usually joined to a second polynucleotide chain to form a double helix
DNA	c.	has four kinds of bases, GCAT
RNA	d.	has four kinds of bases, GCAU
both	e.	can form G-C base pairs
RNA	f.	forms A-U base pairs
DNA	g.	sugar in nucleotides is deoxyribose
both	h.	a nucleic acid
DNA	i.	deoxyribonucleic acid
RNA	j.	ribonucleic acid

a. both;   b. DNA;   c. DNA;   d. RNA;   e. both;   f. RNA;
g. DNA;   h. both;   i. DNA;   j. RNA

130. Three kinds of RNA participate in the DNA synthesis process. Each one assumes a different role.

messenger RNA
ribosomal RNA
transfer RNA

Associate the name of each kind of RNA with its function,
described below:

_m_	a.	the RNA that moves from DNA to ribosomes carrying DNA's base-coded message
_r_	b.	the RNA that unites with about 50 proteins to form the actual sites of

protein construction, which are the
cell organelles, called ribosomes

_____ c.   the RNA that transfers amino acids
to the protein assembly site at the
ribosome

---

a. messenger RNA;   b. ribosomal RNA;   c. transfer RNA

131.

     messenger RNA   ribosomal RNA   transfer RNA
        mRNA   rRNA   tRNA

The three kinds of RNA assisting DNA in protein synthesis are
often abbreviated as shown above. Which kind of RNA, in combination with protein, forms the cytoplasmic organelles that serve
as the sites at which amino acids are joined to form proteins?

What are these cytoplasmic structures called?

---

ribosomal RNA or rRNA; ribosomes

132. To carry DNA's instructions for protein building from the
nucleus to the ribosomal construction sites in the cytoplasm, cells
use a second kind of RNA, *messenger RNA,* or *mRNA.* Messenger
RNA is formed by base pairing with the gene strand of an open
segment of DNA. This process is called *transcription.*

a.   In the formation of messenger RNA, G and C bases pair as
they do in DNA replication. What RNA base pairs with
DNA's A?
What mRNA base series would be produced by the DNA
sequence CGAAAT?

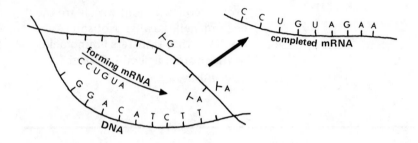

b. The DNA molecule above contains the triplet codons GGA, CAT, and CTT, specifying, respectively, the amino acids pro, val, and glu. What are the messenger RNA codons for these amino acids? _CCU_ , _GUA_ , _GAA_

---

a. U; GCUUUA;   b. CCU; GUA, GAA

133. Copying a message without significantly changing its form is called *transcription.*

Changing a message from one language to another language (English→French) is called *translation.*

a. Is the base-to-base change involved in DNA's making mRNA most like transcription or translation? _transcription_

b. Which of these terms best describes the base-to-amino acid change involved in mRNA's making protein? _translation_

---

a. transcription;   b. translation

134. Although DNA is the "master molecule" directing protein production, the triplet ~~codons~~ for amino acids were first worked out using artificial mRNA. At the top of the next page is a chart of mRNA codons for amino acids.

Second Base					
	U	C	A	G	
U	UUU ⎱ phe UUC ⎰ UUA UUG	UCU ⎱ UCC ⎰ ser UCA UCG	UAU ⎱ tyr UAC ⎰ UAA ⎱ STOP UAG ⎰	UGU ⎱ cys UGC ⎰ UGA STOP UGG try	U C A G
C	CUU ⎱ leu CUC CUA CUG	CCU ⎱ CCC CCA ⎰ pro CCG	CAU ⎱ his CAC ⎰ CAA ⎱ gln CAG ⎰	CGU ⎱ CGC CGA ⎰ arg CGG	U C A G
A	AUU ⎱ AUC ⎰ ile AUA AUG met; START	ACU ⎱ ACC ACA ⎰ thr ACG	AAU ⎱ asn AAC ⎰ AAA ⎱ lys AAG ⎰	AGU ⎱ ser AGC ⎰ AGA ⎱ arg AGG ⎰	U C A G
G	GUU ⎱ GUC GUA ⎰ val GUG START	GCU ⎱ GCC GCA ⎰ ala GCG	GAU ⎱ asp GAC ⎰ GAA ⎱ glu GAG ⎰	GGU ⎱ GGC GGA ⎰ gly GGG	U C A G

First Base (left) — Third Base (right)

a. What amino acid has the mRNA triplet code name UUU?
___phe___ What sequence of amino acids would be
produced by molecules of artificial mRNA with the sequence
UUUUUUUUU? _phephephe_ What DNA sequence
would produce the UUUUUUUUU sequence? _aaaaaaaaa_

b. What do the start (AUG, GUG) and stop (UAA, UAG, UGA)
codons mean? _beginning & end of protein_

---

a. phe (phenylalanine); phe-phe-phe; AAAAAAAAA;   b. start or
stop making a particular protein (These would be the first and last
triplet codons in a gene-copied sequence of mRNA. They are like
punctuation in the English language, in which a capital letter
denotes the start of a sentence, and a period, the end of a sentence.)

135. A DNA gene strand coding for the production of an average
protein might contain about 1,500 bases. How many bases would
the mRNA that was copied from such a gene contain?
_1,500_

Sometimes, one mRNA molecule is formed as a copy of a group of related genes (an operon). If each gene in the operon was average size, how many bases would be contained in mRNA copied from an operon with four genes? _6,000_

1,500; 6,000 (4 x 1,500) (one mRNA base is placed by one DNA base.)

136. Once messenger RNA has been transcribed by base pairing with a DNA gene strand, mRNA leaves the nucleus and attaches to organelles that synthesize protein in the cytoplasm. What are these structures, composed of proteins and ribosomal RNA molecules, called? _ribosomes_

organelles of

---

ribosomes

137. Ribosomes are responsible for reading mRNA's base series properly and in order from start to stop codons.

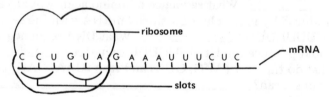

As the diagram shows, ribosomes have two slots for holding two groups of three bases. What are groups of three bases of mRNA called? _Codons_ During translation, each group of three bases represents a code name for an _amino acid._ What would happen without ribosomes to read mRNA triplets properly?

mess

triplet codons; amino acid; *Sample answer:* Without ribosomes, the mRNA codons might be read out of order, or might be read from the wrong starting point, as diagramed below:

138.

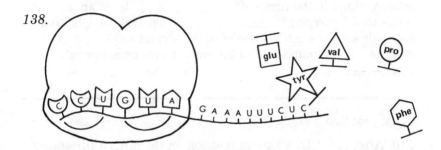

Messenger RNA attached to a ribosome has access to thousands of amino acids, which are continually made available from food taken into the cell. Do these amino acids have any means of base pairing directly with their mRNA codons?___*no*___

no (Just as we are unable to recognize our names written in an unfamiliar alphabet, amino acids have no chemical means of recognizing their base code names.)

139. To bring amino acids together with their proper ribosome-bound mRNA triplet codons, there exists a *third* kind of RNA, *transfer RNA*, or *tRNA*.

Transfer RNA is a cloverleaf-shaped molecule of 70-90 nucleotides with an amino acid attachment at one end and a triplet codon or *anticodon* for base pairing with ribosome-bound mRNA at the other end.

In the diagram above, what tRNA triplet is base-paired to the mRNA triplet in the first slot? _G G A_ What amino acid is this tRNA carrying? _pro_ What tRNA triplet *will* base pair with the mRNA triplet in the second slot? _C A U_ Will the second amino acid in the chain above be glu or val? _val_

GGA; pro; CAU; val

140. After two tRNA's are in position on the mRNA-ribosome complex, three things happen: (1) the amino acids on the ribosomes join to start a protein chain, (2) the first tRNA is released for possible reuse, and (3) the ribosome moves along to the next mRNA triplet.

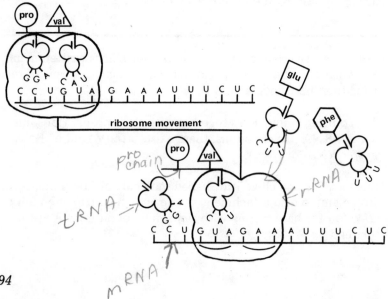

On the diagrams at the bottom of page 94,

a. label the tRNA just released and the protein chain that is just starting to assemble;

b. draw in the tRNA-amino acid complex that will be attracted to the new mRNA triplet now in place in the second slot.

Sample answer:

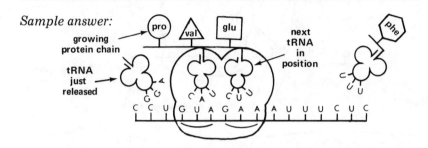

141. As the ribosome continues to move along the mRNA, the protein chain originally specified by DNA spins off the ribosome. On the diagram below, label (a) the *protein* molecule, (b) the *DNA* specifying its production, and (c) the three kinds of *RNA—ribosomal*, *messenger*, and *transfer*.

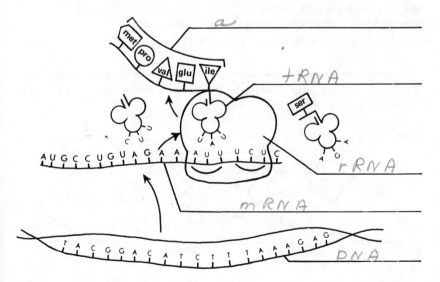

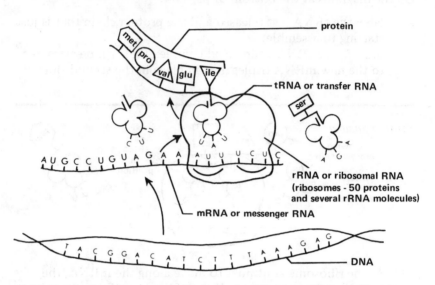

protein

tRNA or transfer RNA

rRNA or ribosomal RNA
(ribosomes - 50 proteins
and several rRNA molecules)

mRNA or messenger RNA

DNA

142. From the answer just diagramed, consider the first (farthest left) triplet codon of DNA in the nucleus.

What is the first DNA triplet indicated? ___*TAC*___ What mRNA triplet will it produce by base pairing? ___*AUG*___ What tRNA triplet will pair with this mRNA triplet? ___*UAC*___ What amino acid would this tRNA carry? ___*tyr*___

TAC; AUG; UAC; met (Refer to the mRNA codon chart and check the relationship of mRNA and the amino acid met.)

143.

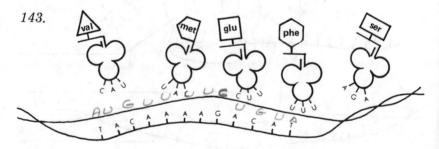

The diagram at the bottom of page 96 is of a portion of a DNA gene strand and several amino acids bound by tRNA. What mRNA base sequence would be produced by this gene strand? _____ _____ What amino acid sequence (protein) would result? _____

AUGUUUUCUGUA; met-phe-ser-val

144. Sometimes additional ribosomes start to read along messenger RNA in a sequence, forming a *polyribosome*, or *polysome*. A polysome is visible with an electron microscope.

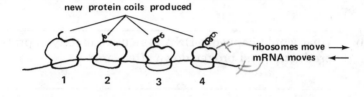

new protein coils produced

ribosomes move →
mRNA moves ←

1   2   3   4

a. On the above diagram of a polysome, label the mRNA strand and one of the ribosomes.
b. If the ribosomes are moving from left to right, which ribosome has produced the longest protein chain? ___4___

---

a.

ribosome

mRNA

b. 4 (The longest coil of protein is at the top of ribosome 4, the one farthest from the starting point.)

145. Ribosomes can join amino acids at the incredible rate of two per second. At this rate, how long would it take a pancreatic cell to form insulin, a small protein consisting initially of 84 amino acids? ___42 sec___

only 42 seconds (84 ÷ 2)

146. When ribosomes have finished reading an mRNA molecule, the protein is released to function, and the mRNA is broken down (digested into nucleotide subunits).

a. What would happen if the mRNA were not broken down immediately?

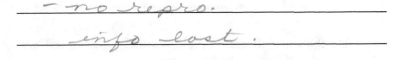

con't reading

over production

b. What would happen if DNA were used directly in protein production and broken down afterward?

‾ no repro.

info lost .

Sample answers: a. If mRNA were not broken down soon after assembling protein, other ribosomes might begin reading it and produce more copies of the same protein, causing an overproduction of that protein.   b. If DNA were broken down after protein production, the base code information for that protein would be permanently lost; thus, mRNA is an intermediary that protects the genetic information of DNA for future protein synthetic activities.

147. The past several frames have reviewed the process by which the hereditary information of DNA is used to build a specific protein with a given function.

98

a. Although the term *translation* may be used to refer generally
to the overall process by which DNA ultimately specifies the
amino acid sequence of a protein, translation more specifically refers to only those steps involving base-R group (amino
acid) relationships, and the term *transcription* refers to purely
base-base relationships, In this more specific sense, then,
messenger RNA formation is called (translation/transcription)
___script___, and the events occurring at the ribosome are
called ___elation___.

b. Three RNA molecules are involved in the translation process,
each with a name describing its role.
(1) Which RNA carries the hereditary information of DNA
from nucleus to cytoplasmic ribosomes? ___mr___
(2) Which RNA combines with protein to form the sites
where proteins are assembled? ___r___
(3) Which RNA moves amino acids into the places specified
by triplet codons on ribosomes? ___t___

---

a. transcription; translation;   b. (1) messenger RNA (mRNA);
(2) ribosomal RNA (rRNA); (3) transfer RNA (tRNA)

148. Review the process of DNA regulation of protein synthesis
by marking the following from 1 (first) to 5 (last) to indicate
their order of occurrence.

___5___a. protein released from ribosome to function
___4___b. amino acids join to form a protein as ribosome moves
down
___3___c. tRNA molecules bring in the specific amino acids called
for by mRNA
___2___d. mRNA forms by base pairing with DNA gene strand and
moves from nucleus to ribosomes
___1___e. segment of DNA double helix unzips to expose the base
sequence of a gene strand

---

a. 5;   b. 4;   c. 3;   d. 2;   e. 1

149. Indicate the appropriate kind(s) of RNA referred to by each of the statements below.

*m*_____a.   long strand of nucleotides, usually containing several hundred triplet codons

*t*_____b.   small, folded, cloverleaf-shaped RNA with three of its bases serving as a triplet codon or anti-codon

*r*_____c.   large RNA that associates with proteins to form protein assembling structures

*m*_____d.   carries base sequence information from DNA in the nucleus to ribosomes in the cytoplasm

*r*_____e.   part of structure that assists in reading mRNA three bases at a time

*t*_____f.   brings amino acids specified by mRNA

*m*_____g.   usually broken down after it is used to make one or a few proteins

r & *t*__h.   two RNA's used over and over many times

*t*_____i.   without this RNA, amino acids would not recognize the appropriate mRNA codons

*r*_____j.   without this RNA, mRNA would not be oriented properly as triplet codons

---

a. mRNA;   b. tRNA;   c. rRNA;   d. mRNA;   e. rRNA;
f. tRNA;   g. mRNA;   h. tRNA and rRNA (either order);
i. tRNA;   j. rRNA

150. In this chapter, the process of protein production from information encoded in DNA has been described. Because this process occurs in all living organisms, knowledge of the process has been valuable for the treatment of some diseases.

Antibiotics stop the growth of harmful bacteria by interfering with the production of proteins essential for bacterial growth. The examples at the top of the next page show how such interference may occur.

(1) *puromycin*—interferes with the arrival of amino acids at the ribosome;

(2) *actinomycin D*—blocks the transmission of base information from nucleus to ribosomes;

(3) *streptomycin*—prevents union of amino acids to form protein chains.

According to these descriptions, the function of which of the three kinds of RNA is blocked by puromycin? _transfer_ .. by actinomycin D? _messenger_. by streptomycin? _ribosomal_

---

transfer or tRNA; messenger or mRNA; ribosomal rRNA (in the sense that rRNA is part of the ribosome structure; actually, it is one of the ribosomal proteins that is affected by streptomycin)

151. Certain features distinguish mRNA, tRNA, and rRNA from DNA.

a. What base do RNA molecules furnish to pair with base A instead of DNA's T? _uracil_

b. Do these molecules occur basically as single strands or as double helices? _single_

c. Do nucleotides of these molecules have the sugar ribose, or deoxyribose? _ribose_

d. DNA stands for deoxyribonucleic acid. What does RNA stand for? _____

---

a. U;   b. single strands (with some folded back pairing, especially in the cloverleaf shape of tRNA);   c. ribose;   d. ribonucleic acid

152. Some viruses, such as the flu virus and tobacco mosaic virus, contain RNA *instead* of DNA.

a. Is RNA as *potentially* capable of coding hereditary information as DNA is? _yes_

b. Could viral RNA be used to direct protein production in a cell taken over by a virus? _____
c. Is it conceivable that RNA could be used to direct the production of DNA? _____
d. In cell cultures, could the action of such viruses be blocked by antibiotics? _____

---

a. yes;   b. yes;   c. yes (This actually does occur in rare instances.); d. yes (Since numerous antibiotics interfere with various RNA functions, certain antibiotics could be effective in cell culture, but the antibiotics would block normal protein production in the cell, damaging or killing it. Thus, antibiotics cannot be used against viral infection in living organisms.)

153. In your own words, describe the roles of m-, r-, and tRNA molecules, and indicate the significance of this knowledge.

_____

_____

_____

_____

_____

_____

_____

_____

_____

Sample answer: The m-, r-, and tRNA molecules make possible the translation of information encoded by DNA into the protein molecules responsible for cell function and the development of specific traits. By carrying DNA's information to the cytoplasm, mRNA allows DNA to remain "protected" in the nucleus. rRNA and proteins form the ribosomes that read mRNA triplets properly and in order. tRNA brings in the specific amino acids called for by mRNA bound to ribosomes.

The development of antibiotics that block the growth of harmful bacteria by interfering with the function of various kinds of RNA is one valuable way in which an understanding of DNA-RNA-protein relationships has been useful to mankind.

Summary

Three kinds of RNA molecules are involved in the basic life process by which inherited DNA directs the synthesis of structural and functional proteins. RNA is a nucleic acid, as is DNA, but the sugar of RNA's nucleotides is ribose, instead of DNA's deoxyribose, and RNA has the base uracil, instead of DNA's thymine, for pairing with adenine.

The three kinds of RNA assisting in DNA-protein synthesis are ribosomal, messenger, and transfer RNA. Along with about 50 different proteins, ribosomal RNA forms the relatively large particles called ribosomes. Ribosomes are the sites in the cytoplasm at which amino acids are assembled to form proteins. Messenger RNA, derived by base pairing with a gene or operon of DNA, carries DNA's instructions to the ribosome to direct the proper alignment of the amino acids. Transfer RNA molecules actually bring specific amino acids, for which they have a triplet codon, to the ribosomal site for assembling proteins.

Some antibiotics are effective in killing or stopping bacterial growth because they interfere with the function of mRNA, tRNA or rRNA.

1. In the abbreviations DNA and RNA, what does NA stand for? *nucleic acid* The D (deoxyribose) and R (ribose) stand for the sugar part of the nucleotide that is different for DNA and RNA because one atom of one element is missing from DNA that is present in RNA. What element is this? *oxygen*

2. The four most common bases of DNA are known by the letters GCAT. What are RNA's four bases? *G*, *C*, *A*, *U* Which of RNA's bases pairs with A? *U*

3. The abbreviations mRNA, tRNA, and rRNA stand, respectively, for *messenger* RNA, *transfer* RNA, and *ribosomal* RNA.

4. The composite diagram below summarizes the major steps in DNA regulation of protein synthesis. Label (a) the DNA, (b) the protein, and (c) the three kinds of RNA assisting in the process.

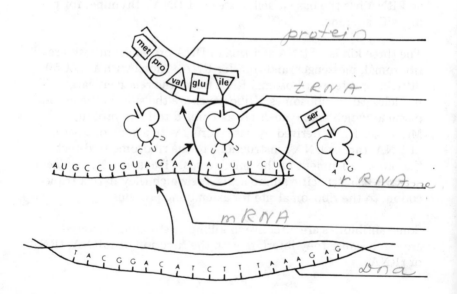

5. Write the name of the appropriate type(s) of RNA for each
    description below.

    ____m____a. formed as a base copy of a DNA gene or operon
    ____m____b. a long molecule that is moved through one end
                of a ribosome (at about two codons per second)
                while a newly formed protein molecule is being
                released from the other end of the ribosome
    ____r____c. very large molecules that associate with about
                50 proteins to form the cytoplasmic organelles
                at which proteins are assembled
    ____r____d. forms the structure that holds messenger RNA
                so that its bases can be read in a correct orienta-
                tion as triplet codons
    ____t____e. relatively small molecule that carries amino
                acids, and base pairs with messenger RNA
    ____t____f. about 70-90 small nucleotides shaped like a
                folded cloverleaf and carrying a triplet codon
                for one specific amino acid
    ____m____g. read a few times to make a few copies of one
                particular protein, then broken down
    __r_&_t_h. two molecules used over and over again in mak-
                ing many different kinds of protein

6. By numbering from the first (1) to the last (6), arrange the
    following in the order of their occurrence.

    __1__a. gene strand of DNA unzips from its copy strand
    __6__b. protein released from one end of ribosome to per-
            form some structural or functional task, mRNA
            released from other end to be read a few more times
            or broken down
    __2__c. mRNA formed by base pairing with DNA
    __3__d. mRNA attaches to the ribosome
    __4__e. a tRNA brings an amino acid to the ribosome
    __5__f. amino acids joined, tRNA released for reuse, and
            ribosome moves to next mRNA triplet codon

105

7. Inherited DNA base sequences direct the construction of trait-producing structural and functional proteins. In your own words, what are the roles of mRNA, tRNA, and rRNA in this process?

8.   Of what practical value is our knowledge of the regulation
     of protein synthesis by DNA?

_____

_____

_____

_____

_____

Check your answers against those on pages 146 and 147.

V
DNA-PROTEIN SYNTHESIS: ROLES OF ENZYMES AND REGULATORS

Introduction

In the previous chapter, you saw how RNA molecules in DNA-protein synthesis. This chapter describes the role of enzymes in this process, and the role of regulators in turning DNA on and off.

The role of enzymes in DNA-protein synthesis is especially interesting because enzymes are proteins. This means that specific proteins are needed to make other specific proteins, and it raises questions about what life is and how it originated.

Genetic engineers place much value on the study of DNA regulators. For example, cells in an amputated limb contain all the DNA information for regrowth of the limb. Salamanders are often able to do this, but human DNA for doing the same thing is apparently "turned off." Some researchers believe we can discover ways to turn on DNA so that regrowth of amputated human limbs is possible.

Upon completing this chapter, you should be able to:

- explain the role played by enzymes, especially activating enzymes, in DNA-protein synthesis, and discuss the implications the role of enzymes may have for our concepts of the nature and origin of life.

- explain the role played by regulators, especially operon repressors and inducers, in DNA-protein synthesis, and discuss the applications the role of regulators may have in the future of genetic engineering.

154. Base pairing plays a key role in DNA-protein synthesis, but it does not account for everything. Mark the following "yes" if they involve base pairing or "no" if they do not.

_no_ a. unzipping of a segment of the DNA double helix
yes b. DNA's production of mRNA
_no_ c. mRNA's attachment to a ribosome
yes d. tRNA's recognition of ribosome-bound mRNA triplet codons
_no_ e. tRNA's binding with a specific amino acid

---

a. no;   b. yes;   c. no;   d. yes;   e. no

155. Generally, those processes in DNA-protein synthesis that do not involve base pairing do involve enzymes or regulators. Would base pairing, then, or some enzyme or regulator be involved in the union of mRNA and tRNA? _base_ ... of tRNA and amino acids? _enzyme_

---

base pairing;   *Sample answer:*   some enzyme or regulator

156. Enzymes are large protein molecules that attract other molecules and hold them in "lock-and-key" slots for rapid reaction.

a.   Which of the four shapes—A, B, C, or D—would be attracted and held for reaction by the enzyme diagramed below?
_A_ and _D_

ENZYME   A   B   C   D

b.   Molecules may combine *directly* by means of their own interlocking shapes, or they may combine *indirectly* by interlocking with a third molecule. Which involves indirect interlocking combinations—base pairing, or enzyme action? _enzyme act_ Which involves direct interlocking? _base_

a. A and D;   b. enzyme action; base pairing

157. If the enzyme forming DNA polymers is called DNA polymerase, then what will the enzyme forming RNA polymers be called?
RNA polymerase (Hint: --- ase)

RNA polymerase

158. When a DNA double helix opens up, it can make either more
DNA (replication), or it can make mRNA (transcription). The
"choice" is controlled by enzymes.

a. Which enzyme—DNA or RNA polymerase—would start the
    replication process? _DNA poly_ ... the transcrip-
    tion process? _RNA poly_
b. Messenger RNA formation, the first step in protein synthesis,
    is often called transcription, and the enzyme involved,
    transcriptase. Which of the two polymerases above is equiva-
    lent to transcriptase? _RNA poly_ Which might
    be called "replicase"? _DNA poly_
c. The antibiotic actinomycin D blocks the lock-and-key sites
    of RNA polymerase in bacterial cells. Would this antibiotic
    block replication or transcription or both? _trans_

a. DNA polymerase; RNA polymerase;   b. RNA polymerase; DNA
polymerase;   c. *Sample answer:* It would block transcription
directly. (Without protein production, the bacterium would also
be unable to reproduce.)

159. An open DNA double helix can make either more DNA or
mRNA. The choice is made by large proteins called _enzymes_

Sample answers: enzymes (in general), or DNA and RNA polymerases (specifically)

160. After it is made by RNA polymerase, an mRNA attaches to a ribosome and base pairs with tRNAs carrying specific amino acids.

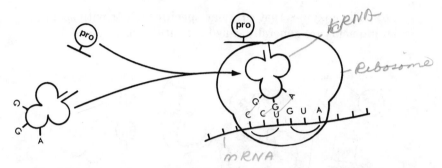

a. Would base pairing enable the GGA tRNA above to selectively combine with the pro amino acid above? _____
b. Chemically, amino acids and tRNAs unite through acid and sugar groups that are common, respectively, to all amino acids and all tRNAs. Would the chemical structures (shapes) of the two molecules, then, enable the GGA tRNA to combine with pro vs. val? _____ *no* _____

---

a. no; b. no

161. The key step in DNA-protein synthesis is the union of specific tRNAs with specific amino acids, and neither base pairing nor inherent chemical properties can explain this step. The union of specific tRNAs and amino acids is brought about instead by special large proteins.

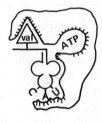

a. What are such proteins called? _____ *enzymes* _____
b. What is the shape of that part of the above enzyme that interlocks with the amino acid R group for valine?
    _____ *△* _____

a. enzymes;　b. *Sample answer:* 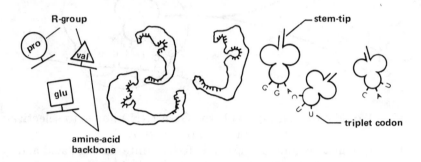 ← interlocking enzyme
R group

162. The enzymes that combine specific tRNAs with specific amino acids are generally called *activating enzymes.*

R-group

pro
val
glu

stem-tip

amine-acid backbone

G
G
A
C
U
U

C
A

triplet codon

Virtually all 20 of the common amino acids have the same amine and acid groups, but each has a different R group. All tRNAs have the same "step-tip" groups, but each has a different triplet codon on the middle "leaf" of its cloverleaf structure. To make specific combinations, an activating enzyme must recognize which part of the amino acid? __R-grp__ ... which part of the tRNA? __triplet codon__

R-group; triplet codon

163. Activating enzymes actually produce chemical combinations between the acid groups of amino acids and the sugar of the terminal tRNA stem-tip group. Would the enzyme *sites* (1) in diagram above for making these acid-sugar combinations be specific for a certain tRNA-amino acid pair, or nonspecific? __non-specific__

nonspecific

112

164. Activating enzymes have two specific sites interlocking with or "recognizing" an R group and a triplet codon, and they have two nonspecific sites for recognizing acids and sugars. In addition to these, activating enzymes have a site recognizing ATP, a molecule which supplies energy for the tRNA-amino acid combination. How many lock-and-key recognition sites, then, does an activating enzyme have in total? _____ 5 _____

---

five (for R group, triplet codon, acid, sugar, and ATP)

165. The following diagram shows an enzyme that plays a crucial role in DNA-protein synthesis, and is rather complicated, with five special activating sites. What is this enzyme called? *activating* The enzyme's active sites are for holding (one each):

(1)   the *R group* distinctive of each amino acid,
(2)   the *triplet codon* or "anti-codon" distinctive of each tRNA,
(3)   the *acid* of the amino acid, which nonspecifically joins it to the tRNA,
(4)   the *stem-tip* sugar of the tRNA, which nonspecifically joins it to the amino acid, and
(5)   the *ATP* molecule which energizes the coupling of tRNA and its amino acid.

Using the terms given above, label the five sites on the enzyme below:

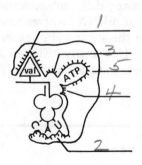

activating;   *Sample answer:*

```
                                    ── R group
                                    ── acid
                          /val\  /ATP\  ── ATP "energizer"
                                    ── stem-tip sugar

                                    ── triplet codon
```

166. The "heart" of the vital DNA-protein synthesis process is matching R groups and base triplets. Can DNA bases line up amino acid R groups directly? ____*no*____ Can mRNA attract particular R groups? ____*no*____ Can tRNA alone find amino acids with specific R groups? ____*no*____ What, then, is the only kind of molecule that can make the life-essential connection between bases and R groups? *activating enzymes*

---

no; no; no; ACTIVATING ENZYMES (Please pardon our emphasis, but it is important to note the activating enzymes that play such an absolutely essential and distinctive role in enabling DNA and protein to work together to make life possible.)

167. There are about 20 amino acids, each with a different R-group, and even more tRNAs, each with a different triplet codon. Therefore, there must be at least how many different activating enzymes? ____*20*____ The production of mRNA involves base pairing and uses RNA polymerase to join the sugar and phosphate groups that are the same for all mRNAs. How many different RNA polymerases do cells need to make their thousands of mRNA polymers? ____*1*____

Sample answer: at least 20;   just one

114

168. In order to make proteins, DNA needs enzymes, including RNA polymerase, activating enzymes, and other enzymes. But these enzymes, like all enzymes, are proteins themselves. Therefore, DNA needs proteins to make proteins. How do you think the DNA-protein relationship first got started? _____

_____

??? You are no doubt just as puzzled by this question. Men are continually speculating about life's origin. Consider the following points of view.

169. Two general viewpoints on the origin of the DNA-protein relationship and the origin of life have influenced western culture:

(1) *evolution*—the concept that the kind of molecular order distinctive of living cells is internally determined, somewhat like the order in a crystal, suggesting that living things gradually developed as an expression of the chemical potential inherent in matter.

(2) *creation*—the concept that the kind of molecular order distinctive of living cells is externally determined, somewhat like the order in a man-made device, suggesting that living things were created by God with features of design not reducible to chemical interactions.

Suppose that genetic engineers were able to make a simple living cell from nonliving chemicals. Would that solve the evolution-creation question? _____

_____

Probably not. Christian creationists could explain that people created in God's image had used their creative talents to accomplish a feat somewhat like God's making life from the dust of the ground. Evolutionists would explain that man's creative accomplishment more or less duplicated some past chemical process.

170. Associate each of the DNA assistants below with one of the following descriptions.

rRNA   DNA polymerase
mRNA   RNA polymerase
tRNA   activating enzymes

m RNA a. carries a base-pair copy of DNA's genetic information from the cell's nucleus to its cytoplasm
r RNA b. forms part of the ribosome particles that read mRNA, three bases at a time
t RNA c. brings to the ribosomes the amino acids called for by mRNA triplet codons
_a - e_ d. effectively translates base language into R-group language by forming specific amino acid-tRNA pairs
RNA poler e. zips together the sugar-phosphate groups of mRNA base paired to unzipped gene strands of DNA
DNA poler f. zips together the backbones of the new gene and copy strands formed during replication

---

a. mRNA;   b. rRNA;   c. tRNA;   d. activating enzymes;
e. RNA polymerase;   f. DNA polymerase

171. Review the sequence of action of protein synthesis assistants by marking the following steps in the process from 1 (first) to 6 (final).

_1_ a.   segment of DNA opens, exposing the base sequence of a gene strand
_6_ b.   a completed protein, its amino acid sequence determined indirectly by inherited DNA, is released from the ribosome
_3_ c.   mRNA leaves DNA and attaches to a ribosome
_2_ d.   RNA polymerase helps form mRNA, which base pairs with DNA
_5_ e.   tRNAs base pair with mRNA
_4_ f.   activating enzymes couple specific tRNAs and amino acids

a. (1); b. (6); c. (3); d. (2); e. (5); f. (4)

172. In addition to the specific assistant molecules above, DNA action also depends on a wide variety of molecules we will call *regulators.* Regulators affect the opening and closing of DNA helices.

a. Are the bases of a DNA gene strand available for mRNA formation when the helix is closed, or when the base pairs are opened? _opened_

b. If a regulator molecule acted to open a segment of DNA, would it be acting to turn on or turn off protein synthesis? _on_ Would a regulator that acted to keep the helix closed effectively turn on or turn off protein production? _off_

a. opened; b. turn on; turn off

173. All of the cells in an adult human body (several *trillion* of them) are descended from the fertilized egg cell, and each cell has a replicated copy of the DNA in that egg cell's chromosomes.

Diagramed below is a portion of DNA from a hypothetical human chromosome, showing some of the proteins and traits related to some of its genes.

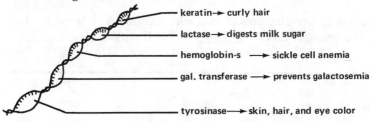

keratin→ curly hair

lactase→ digests milk sugar

hemoglobin-s ⟶ sickle cell anemia

gal. transferase ⟶ prevents galactosemia

tyrosinase→ skin, hair, and eye color

a. Would a liver cell contain the gene for producing curly hair proteins? _yes_ Would a skin cell contain the gene for producing the oxygen-carrying hemoglobin normally found only in red blood cells? _yes_

b.   If the gene for producing the milk-digesting enzyme, lactase, is present in lung cells, do you think it is turned on or turned off? ___*off*___ Would the gene for producing tyrosinase for skin, hair, and eye color be turned on or off in stomach cells? ___*off*___

c.   The factors for turning genes on and off belong to which of these groups of molecules—nucleic acids, enzymes, or regulators? ___*regulators*___

---

a. yes; yes;   b. turned off; turned off;   c. regulators

174. In certain large chromosomes of insects, genes can be associated with bands, and mRNA production can be associated with the "puffing" of these bands.

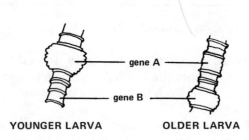

YOUNGER LARVA   OLDER LARVA

According to the diagrams above, which gene—A or B— is turned on in the younger larva? ___*A*___ ... in the older larva? ___*B*___

A; B

175. When chromosomes from an older larva are experimentally placed in cells or cell extracts of younger larva, gene A puffs and gene B "unpuffs." Does this suggest that cells contain molecules capable of turning DNA on and off? ___*yes*___ What are such molecules called? ___*regulators*___

118

What do you think would happen to genes A and B if the younger larva's chromosome were placed in cell extracts of older larvae?

_____

_____

yes; regulators;   *Sample answer:* Gene A would unpuff or turn off, and gene B would puff or turn on, in response to regulators in the cells of older larvae.

176. For some genes in living cells, mRNA production is blocked by proteins called *repressors*. Repressors sometimes block the action of whole sets of related genes called *operons*. When a repressor protein is present, then, is a gene or operon turned on or turned off? ___*off*___ What could happen if the repressor were absent? ___*on*_____

_____

turned off;   *Sample answer:* With the repressor absent, the gene or operon could be turned on.

177. Molecules called *inducers* combine with repressor proteins and block the repressor action. What effect, then, would inducers have on protein production? ___*on*_____

_____

Sample answer: Inducers would turn on protein production (by blocking the repressors that were blocking mRNA production, the first step in protein production).

178. Repressor proteins are produced by special DNA segments called *regulator genes*. Some regulator genes produce only *incomplete repressors* that will not block mRNA production unless first combined with a *co-repressor*.

Mark the following either "on" or "off" to indicate the effect each molecule or pair would have on protein production:

_off__a. repressor protein
_on__b. repressor-inducer combination
_on__c. incomplete repressor
_off__d. incomplete repressor–co-repressor combination

---

a. off;   b. on;   c. on;   d. off

179.   repressor   co-repressor   regulator gene
         incomplete repressor   inducer

Match each of the DNA regulating factors above with one of the statements below:

_reg.___a. produces repressor or incomplete repressor proteins
_rep.___b. a protein that turns off gene action in protein production
_in rep__c. product of a regulator gene that is not effective in blocking gene action by itself
_indu.__d. blocks repressor action, thus turning on DNA-protein synthesis
_co-rep__e. combines with an incomplete repressor to turn gene off

---

a. regulator gene;   b. repressor;   c. incomplete repressor;
d. inducer;   e. co-repressor

180. At the top of the next page is a photograph of the *lac operon*, a group of genes producing enzymes for transporting, digesting, and utilizing lactose, or milk sugar. The photograph shows the operon turned off, and the diagram represents it turned on.

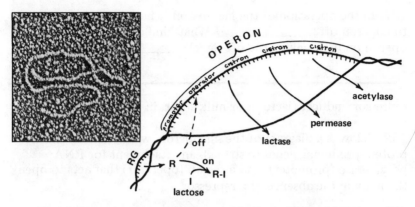

a. The operon gene is off when the helix is (zipped/unzipped) _zip_____, and on when it is _unzip_.

b. The off signal is a repressor labeled R in the diagram. What gene, labeled RG, produces the repressor? _regulator gene_ Is the RG gene part of the operon, or located at some distance from it? (part of/separate) _sep_____

c. The action of the repressor protein is shown blocked by combination with a molecule labeled I. What does I stand for? _inducer_ In this case, the I molecule is lactose (milk sugar), the very molecule that is used up by the action of the enzymes produced by the operon. When the lactose has been used up, will the operon be on or off? _off_____

d. Bacteria with the operon above are capable of growing on milk sugar. When there is no milk sugar in their growth medium, will they be producing the three enzymes for using milk sugar? _no_____ Will they produce these enzymes when milk sugar is added to their growth medium? _yes_ ... when they use up the added milk sugar? _no_____

e. In summary, the effect of lactose on the repressor protein means that lactose-utilizing enzymes are produced (all the time/never/only when needed) _only when needed_.

---

a. closed, open; b. regulator gene; separate; c. inducer; off;
d. no; yes; no; e. only when needed

181. In the operation of the lac operon, what molecule turns
the operon off? *repressor* What kind of molecule turns the
operon on by blocking the off signal? *inducer*

---

repressor; inducer (lactose, or milk sugar, in this case)

182. Below is a diagram of the *his* operon, which includes nine
protein-producing genes (cistrons), an attachment for RNA
polymerase (promoter), and a region (operator) that acts to open
the helix in the absence of a repressor.

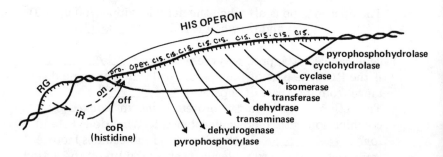

The *his* operon regulator gene diagramed here produces an incomplete repressor, labeled iR. In the absence of other factors, then,
will the operon be on or off? _____ *on* _____ When the incomplete repressor combines with the co-repressor, labeled coR,
what effect does this have on operon function? _____ *off* _____

The co-repressor in this case is histidine (his) itself, the molecule
produced by the nine enzymatic proteins coded for by the nine
operon genes. When histidine is abundant in the cell, will the his
operon be active? _____ *no* _____ When cells run low on his, none
will be left to combine with iR. Will the cell then open and start
making histidine again? _____ *yes* _____

---

on;   *Sample answer:* turns off the operon;   no;   yes

183. What are groups of related genes that are turned on and off together called? _operons_ What are the regulating proteins called that turn genes or gene sets on and off? _complete or incomplete repressors_

---

operons; *Sample answer:* complete and incomplete repressors

184.

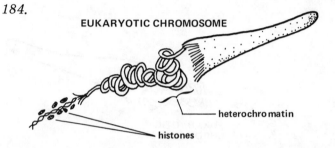

EUKARYOTIC CHROMOSOME

heterochromatin

histones

In bacteria and viruses, repressors bind to the "naked" loops of DNA that constitute the prokaryotic chromosomes in those organisms.

a. In the eukaryotic chromosomes of plants, animals, and human beings, DNA is coated with proteins, especially those called *histones.* Is it possible that these histones could play the role of repressors? _yes_
b. When histones are added to active DNA solutions, DNA activity slows down. When histone blocking factors are added, DNA activity increases. Do these experimental observations suggest histones may act as repressors? _yes_

---

a. yes (and histones do seem to play a repressor or regulatory role); b. yes

NOTE: Prokaryotic and eukaryotic may also be spelled pro-caryotic and eucaryotic.

185. Some regions of chromosomes, called *heterochromatin*, consist of tight, supercoiled loops of protein-coated DNA. Do you think heterochromatin would be active or inactive in protein synthesis? _inactive_

---

inactive (since DNA must be uncoiled or unzipped to be active, and there is evidence that heterochromatic regions are inactive)

186.

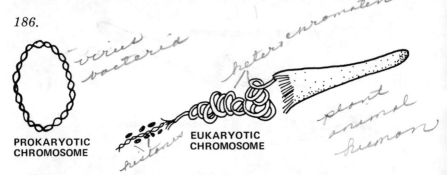

PROKARYOTIC CHROMOSOME

EUKARYOTIC CHROMOSOME

The naked loops of DNA in viruses and bacterial cells are called prokaryotic chromosomes, and the protein-complexed DNAs of plant, animal, and human cells are called eukaryotic chromosomes. In which kind of chromosomes do DNA-bound histones probably serve as repressors? _Euk._ In which kind of chromosomes are tight, supercoiled, inactive regions called heterochromatin found? _Euk._

---

eukaryotic chromosomes; eukaryotic chromosomes also

187. Which of the two basic kinds of chromosomes are found in viruses and bacteria (check one)?

_____a. eukaryotic chromosomes, which are threads of DNA complexed with an equal or greater amount of protein

__✓__b. prokaryotic chromosomes, which are basically naked (proteinless) loops of DNA

b

188.   repressor   histone

Which of the proteins above acts to turn off operon function in
the prokaryotic, naked loop chromosomes of bacteria and viruses?
repressor Which forms a structural part of the eukaryotic
chromosome of plants, animals, and human beings? *histones*
Which probably serves as the off signal blocking DNA function in
eukaryotic chromosomes? *histones*

---

repressor; histone; histone

189. Eukaryotic chromosomes also contain highly coiled regions
of DNA, which are inactive in mRNA formation. What are these
called? *heterochromatin* Genes of eukaryotic chromosomes can be
turned off either by this tight coiling or by the action of chromosomal proteins called *histones*

---

heterochromatin; histones

190. DNA regulating molecules are of great interest to genetic
engineers. Consider for example, the problem of an amputated
leg. A salamander, with a bone pattern similar to ours, can grow
back an amputated leg. Does this suggest that the DNA information for growing a new leg is present in the cells above the amputated leg? *yes* Although human beings do not grow
back amputated legs, is the DNA for doing so probably in their
body cells? *yes* What do you suppose makes this DNA
inactive? *no*
What do you think a genetic engineer might do in an attempt to
stimulate regrowth of an amputated human leg?

_____

_____

yes;   yes;   *Sample answers:* Something has probably turned off
this DNA.   The genetic engineer might try to find some inducer
to turn on the inactive DNA, although many genes are involved,
and the task would not be easy.

191. Antibiotics are available to block the action of RNA polymerase in harmful bacteria, and scientists are presently learning
to control the action of repressor proteins.

What do these developments suggest concerning the practical
value of knowledge about protein assistants in DNA-protein
translation?

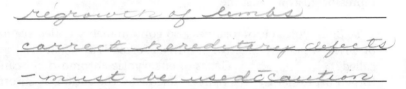

Sample answer: This knowledge has been useful in combating
diseases, and it may one day enable us to stimulate regrowth of
amputated human limbs, or correct hereditary defects. With the
wrong motives, of course, such heredity control could turn from
a blessing to a curse.

192. In this chapter we have emphasized the proteins involved in
DNA-protein synthesis, but enzymatic proteins are also involved
in DNA replication: nuclease, ligase, and DNA polymerase.

a.   Which of these enzymes nicks holes in the DNA double
     helix to start the replication process? *nuclease*
b.   Which zips together the sugar phosphate backbones of
     newly forming polynucleotide gene and copy strands?
     DNA polymerase
c.   Which ties together the loose ends of successively replicated
     DNA segments? *ligase*

nuclease; DNA polymerase; ligase

193. How do nuclease, ligase, and polymerase enzymes function in DNA repair? What is the significance of this repair process?

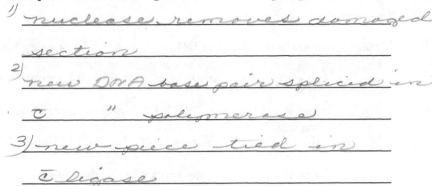

1) nuclease removes damaged section
2) new DNA base pair spliced in c̄ " polymerase
3) new piece tied in c̄ ligase

Sample answer: In DNA repair, the damaged or mutated section of DNA is cut out by the nuclease, a new segment of DNA is base-paired in and spliced together by polymerase, and the new piece is tied into the rest of the DNA chain by ligase.

This repair process prevents much of the hereditary damage mutations might otherwise cause. Genetic engineers may one day be able to turn the repair process on and off, a most useful tool in the correction of inherited defects, the repair of damaged organs and limbs, and a host of other things that remain for now in the realm of science fiction.

194. The enzymatic proteins influencing protein synthesis, replication, and repair certainly interest genetic engineers, but so do the regulatory proteins that function in turning DNA on and off.

a. What kind of protein, the product of a regulatory gene, turns off operon function in the prokaryotic chromosomes of bacteria and viruses? repressor's

b.   What kind of protein, which is bound to DNA as part of
     chromosome structure, blocks gene function in eukaryotic
     chromosomes? _histones_

---

a. repressor;   b. histone

195. Below are some things genetic engineers might one day hope
to accomplish and some things already accomplished as of this
writing. Put a check in front of those things already accomplished.

___✓_a.   use of antibiotics to block DNA-protein translation in
          harmful bacteria
___✓_b.   use of a virus to splice in the DNA needed to cure
          galactosemia in human tissue culture cells
_____c.   use of virus to add the tyrosinase-producing DNA
          needed to correct albinism in human beings
___✓_d.   cloning of multiple frog "twins" by transplant of
          nuclei from frog intestinal lining cells into enucleated
          egg cells
_____e.   use of electric current to turn on genes needed for re-
          growth of an amputated human limb
_____f.   use of repair enzymes to cut out the wrong base in the
          sickle cell gene and splice in the correct one

---

a, b, d (as of this writing, anyway)

Summary

Although DNA may be called the key to life because of its central role in reproduction and trait development, DNA is also a helpless and passive molecule, completely dependent upon proteins and RNA for its function and dependent upon regulators to turn it on and off at appropriate times, making life the key to DNA.

The three kinds of RNA assisting in DNA function (messenger, transfer, and ribosomal RNA) were discussed in the previous chapter. This chapter concerned the proteins assisting in DNA function, including several lock-and-key-acting enzyme proteins. Some of these are the DNA polymerase vital to DNA replication, the RNA polymerase functioning in mRNA formation, the highly complex activating enzymes that join specific tRNAs and amino acids, and some of the DNA regulators.

Some genes act, not singly, but in logical groupings called operons. Most operons are controlled by complete or incomplete repressor proteins produced by special regulator genes. A repressor acts to keep an operon's DNA helix closed (turned off) until an inducer molecule combines with the repressor and inactivates it. Incomplete repressors are inactive and allow their operon to function until the repressor is combined with a co-repressor. The two molecules together can turn off the operon.

By such means, different DNA genes and operons are turned off in one cell and on in another. This helps to explain how a fertilized egg cell develops into an organism that has many different kinds of cells, even though these cells all have the same DNA. Learning how to turn DNA on and off could enable genetic engineers to correct many hereditary defects and even to stimulate regrowth of injured limbs or organs. Some genetic engineers are working toward such "miracles" right now. Such work may also bring us to a better understanding of the nature and origin of life.

Review Quiz

1. Match each of the enzymes below with the role it plays in
    DNA function:

    (1) DNA polymerase, (2) RNA polymerase, and (3) activa-
    ting enzymes.

    _____a. has slots for both particular triplet base codons and
    particular R groups, thus making the coupling of
    specific tRNAs with specific amino acids possible
    _____b. joins the new nucleotides that are based paired to
    the gene and copy strands during DNA replication
    _____c. selects RNA rather than DNA nucleotides for making
    messenger RNA

2. Mark the following processes as most directly involving base
    pairing, enzymes, or regulators.

    _____a. unzipping the DNA double helix
    _____ b. alignment of mRNA with DNA
    _____c. tying DNA strands together
    _____d. tRNA's binding with a specific amino
    acid
    _____e. tRNA's recognition of mRNA triplet
    codons on the ribosomes
    _____f. turning off an operon
    _____g. building the RNA backbone

3. When two molecules do not have interlocking or comple-
    mentary shapes, they are more likely to combine indirectly.
    What type of protein molecule assists in this indirect inter-
    locking? _____ What is the name of the direct
    process by which mRNA triplets interlock with tRNA trip-
    lets? _____

4. What name is given to a group of genes, turned on and off
    together, that produce a group of logically related proteins?
    _____

5. The lac operon, which produces three proteins for trans-
    porting, digesting, and utilizing the milk sugar lactose, is
    turned off by a protein from a regulator gene, until that
    protein is inactivated by lactose.

    a. What general name is given to the protein produced by
        the regulator gene above? _____
    b. What specific molecule above is acting indirectly to
        turn on the lac operon? _____ What is such
        a molecule, acting to inactivate the regulator gene's
        protein, called? _____
    c. When the lactose is used up (transported, digested, and
        utilized), will the operon then be on or off? _____
    d. Would a cell living in an environment with no lactose
        be making proteins for using lactose? _____

6. The his operon produces nine proteins, all involved in the
    production of an important molecule, histidine. The operon
    is normally on, until a buildup of histidine combines with a
    regulator gene's protein to turn the operon off.

    a. What general name is given to a protein like the one
        produced by the regulator gene above? _____
        _____
    b. What molecule activates the regulator gene's protein?
        _____ What, in general, is such a
        molecule called? _____
    c. Would the his operon be on or off in a cell with an
        ample supply of histidine? _____ ... in a cell
        that had used up most of its histidine? _____

7. Each cell formed by a given fertilized egg cell gets a replicated
    copy of the same DNA. In your body, all the cells have the
    same DNA. Why don't all of your cells have the same traits,
    instead of some forming hair, others digestive enzymes, etc.?

    _____

    _____

8. When certain salamanders have a leg cut off, some cells in the cut stump seem to become embryonic again and reactivate their DNA to develop a new leg. Could human beings do that?

_____

_____

_____

9. Briefly, what are some of the things genetic engineers may someday be able to accomplish with their knowledge of DNA?

_____

_____

_____

_____

_____

10. The following are some of the factors which genetic engineers and other scientists may use to influence DNA function. Match each factor with its related process below.

      antibiotics   on-off regulators   viruses
      cloning   repair enzymes

_____a. act to correct base sequence mutations caused by ultraviolet radiation

_____b. used to transplant a missing gene into human tissue culture cells, curing galactosemia

_____c. transplanting cell nuclei to produce multiple copies of a certain frog

_____d. used to stimulate regrowth of an amputated frog limb

_____e. block action of various RNA molecules and enzymes in DNA-protein translation

Check your answers against those on pages 147 and 148.

Unit Quiz

1. Below are replicated structures extracted from the nucleus of a human cell about to reproduce itself. Encoded in these structures is all the information necessary to form a complete human being.

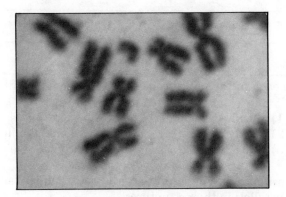

   a.   What are the nuclear structures diagramed above called? _____

   b.   What molecule in these structures encodes the information for forming all the hereditary traits of an individual human being? _____

   c.   What molecule enables these structures to replicate, or make copies of themselves, so that each daughter cell produced by cellular reproduction will be able to develop a full set of hereditary traits? _____

2. Although DNA stores information for producing and perpetuating hereditary traits, DNA acts indirectly through protein molecules.

    a. Discuss sickle cell anemia and illustrate the relationship of hereditary traits to DNA and protein molecules.

_____

_____

_____

_____

_____

_____

_____

_____

    b. Match each of the proteins below to its related trait.

        ____(1) sickle cell anemia   A. keratin
        ____(2) curly hair   B. hemoglobin
        ____(3) galactosemia   C. transferase

3. The relationship of DNA and protein is easier to understand because of parallels in their structures.

    a. Both DNA and proteins are chains of repeated molecular units; what are such chains called? _____

    b. acid   amino acid   nucleotide   R group
        amine   base   phosphate   sugar

        Using the terms listed above, complete the chart at the top of the next page comparing the structures of DNA and protein molecules.

	Monomer	Two Backbone Groups	Side Group
DNA			
Protein			

4. base   gene   operon
    chromosome   genome   triplet codon

DNA's structure enables it to store information for forming
the proteins related to hereditary traits. Match each element
of "DNA language" above with its appropriate description
below.

_____a. one of DNA's four "alphabet letters"
_____b. a DNA "word" identifying one amino acid
_____c. a DNA "sentence" specifying production
                    of a specific protein
_____d. a "paragraph" of DNA directing produc-
                    tion of several functionally related proteins
_____e. a "page" of DNA containing information
                    related to many different traits
_____f. a DNA "book" encoding information for
                    forming all of an organism's hereditary
                    traits

5. Below is one of the four rows in a DNA-protein decoder.
    According to this chart, what amino acid sequence would be
    produced by the DNA base sequence CAACGACTA?

    _____

CAA ⎫	CGA ⎫	CTA ⎫ asp	CCA ⎫
CAG ⎬ val	CGG ⎬ ala	CTG ⎭	CCG ⎬ gly
CAT ⎬	CGT ⎬	CTT ⎫ glu	CCT ⎭
CAC ⎭	CGC ⎭	CTC ⎭	CCC ⎭

135

6. Hereditary information is stored in the base sequence along just one strand of DNA, but DNA normally occurs as two strands paired together and coiled around each other.

   a. What shape is formed by the coiling of the two DNA strands around each other? _____
   b. Pairing of what groups holds the two strands together? _____
   c. What feature of the groups named above enables them to pair? _____
   d. If one strand of DNA contained the base sequence ATGCCA, what sequence would be found in the strand paired with it? _____

7. Before a gene strand can function in protein production, a DNA double helix must be opened or turned on by various regulating factors.

   a. Match the following with the effect each has on turning DNA on and off.

      co-repressor   inducer
      incomplete repressor   repressor

      _____(1) protein produced by a regulator gene that acts to turn off DNA
      _____(2) molecule that blocks repressor action, turning on DNA until the molecule is used up
      _____(3) protein produced by a regulator gene that is not effective in turning off DNA
      _____(4) molecule that combines with an incomplete repressor to block protein production until the molecule is used up

   b. The cells of an amputated limb, like almost all other cells in the human body, have DNA for forming all of a human being's traits. So, why does the limb fail to grow back again? Or, why do liver cells with the DNA for hair fail to produce hair?

_____

_____

_____

8. Once unzipped or turned on, a DNA base sequence uses RNA molecules as assistants in the production of protein.

    a. Is RNA single or double stranded? _____
    b. What base does RNA have for pairing with A? _____
    c. Do RNA nucleotides contain the sugar ribose or deoxyribose? _____
    d. Is RNA ribonucleic acid or deoxyribonucleic acid? _____
    e. What do the initials DNA stand for? _____

9. Three kinds of RNA participate in DNA-protein translation: mRNA, tRNA, and rRNA. What do the initials m, t, and r represent? _____, _____, _____

10. Associate each of the following statements with either mRNA, tRNA, or rRNA.

    _____a. combines with proteins to form ribosomes, the cytoplasmic sites of protein construction
    _____b. formed by base pairing with a gene or operon of DNA
    _____c. small, cloverleaf-shaped molecule carrying a specific triplet codon
    _____d. brings amino acids to the ribosome
    _____e. carries base sequence information from DNA to the ribosome
    _____f. helps to read base sequence information in the proper groups of three bases

137

11. Label the factors involved in DNA-protein translation, as shown in the diagram below.

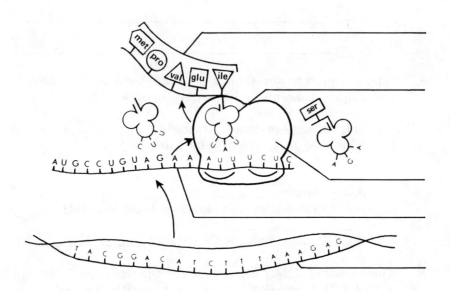

12. Mark the following from 1 to 5 (first to last) to indicate the sequence of events occurring in DNA-protein translation.

_____a.   protein is released from the ribosome to perform a hereditary function dictated ultimately by DNA

_____b.   amino acids join to form a protein as the ribosome moves down the mRNA triplet codons one at a time

_____c.   tRNA molecules "truck in" the specific amino acids called for by ribosome-bound mRNA triplets

_____d.   mRNA forms by base pairing with the DNA gene strand and moves from the nucleus to the ribosome

_____e.   segment of DNA double helix unzips to expose the gene strand base sequence specifying production of a particular protein

138

13.   activating enzymes   RNA polymerase

In addition to using RNA assistants, DNA-protein translation uses large, lock-and-key-acting proteins called enzymes.

a. Which of the two enzymes above joins specific amino acids with specific tRNA molecules?_____
b. Which enables an unzipped DNA double helix to make mRNA, rather than more DNA? _____
c. Which of these makes possible the most crucial step in DNA-protein translation, that of establishing a relationship between R groups and groups of three bases?
_____
d. What question is raised by the necessary participation of such complex and specific proteins in the process by which DNA makes specific proteins? _____

_____

14. DNA molecules make, not only protein molecules, but also more DNA molecules, making DNA the basis of virtually all reproduction.

a. Diagram the replication process as it would occur in the segment of a double helix below.

        ⊢A-T⊣
        ⊢T-A⊣
        ⊢G-C⊣
        ⊢C-G⊣

b. What is it about DNA bases that makes possible the replication of DNA double helices and, hence, the reproduction of living things?

_____

_____

139

15.   ligase   nuclease   polymerase

Although base pairing is the basis of DNA replication, the three enzymes above are also required for the process.

a.   Which of these enzymes starts replication by nicking an opening in the DNA backbone so that bases can unzip? _____

b.   Which zips together the sugar-phosphate backbone of each new strand as its energized nucleotides base pair into proper position? _____

c.   Which ties replicated segments of DNA together to form a long, continuous strand? _____

d.   Is DNA truly a self-reproducing molecule? Explain your answer.

_____

_____

16.

PROKARYOTIC CHROMOSOME

EUKARYOTIC CHROMOSOME

Nuclease-polymerase-ligase and base pairing activities continue one segment at a time until all the DNA in a chromosome is replicated.

a.   Which of the chromosomes above, prokaryotic or eukaryotic, is found in bacteria and viruses? _____

b.   Which chromosome above consists of highly coiled DNA complexed with proteins such as histones?_____

c. When each of an organism's chromosomes is replicated and one copy of each passed on to the daughter cells formed by cell reproduction, will the two daughter cells each be able to develop all the hereditary traits of the single parent cell?_____

17. Occasionally, accidental changes are made in the base sequence of DNA molecules, and the changes can be copied and passed onto future cell generations.

a. What are such changes in DNA base sequences called?

_____

b. What causes such changes? _____
c. What effect do such changes have on proteins and hereditary traits?

_____

d. Are such changes most often harmful or beneficial?

_____

18. It has recently been discovered that some mutations can be repaired by nuclease, polymerase, and ligase enzymes and base pairing. Describe or diagram this process of DNA repair, and comment on its significance.

19. Our growing knowledge of DNA has tempted some scientists to look for ways to use our knowledge to correct hereditary defects and otherwise control DNA and alter normal patterns of reproduction.

   a.   What are such scientists called in popular literature?

   _____

   b.   viruses   repair process
                         cloning   on-off regulators

   These scientists hope to use at least some of the above in DNA control. Match each with one of the items below.

   _____(1)   In the most dramatic example of DNA control to date, scientists used which of the above to transplant into human tissue culture cells the DNA needed to cure galactosemia?
   _____(2)   Which of the above might someday be used to cut out the segment of DNA responsible for sickle cell anemia and splice in the sequence for making normal hemoglobin?
   _____(3)   Which of the above can be controlled in stimulating the amputated limb of a frog to grow back, but have not been so controlled yet with human beings?
   _____(4)   Which of the above has been used to make multiple copies of certain plant and animal organisms and might one day be used with human beings to produce spare tissues or organs or even multiple identical twins?

20.   Concerning the origin of life and the DNA-protein translation process, we have considered the views of evolution and creation. According to which view are the properties of living things extensions of the properties of molecules? _____ According to which view do living things have some externally determined properties that could not be produced by molecular interactions?

_____

Check your answers against those on pages 148 through 150.

Answer Key

Chapter I   DNA, Proteins, and Hereditary Traits

1. (1) b;   (2) a;   (3) c;· (4) d
2. *Sample answer:* Hereditary traits are usually related to certain kinds of protein molecules. These proteins are produced by DNA molecules inherited from the parents. For example, the trait of curly hair depends upon the folding of protein molecules called keratin, which, in turn, are produced by a certain DNA molecule or gene which a person inherits through egg and sperm cells from his parents. (You may, of course, have used sickle cell anemia, albinism, or galactosemia as an example instead of curly hair.)
3. chromosomes;   gene
4. *Sample answer:* Mutations are random changes in DNA (such as those produced by radiation and certain chemicals), and they are important because the changed DNA may change proteins and traits, usually for the worse, as in sickle cell anemia, albinism, or galactosemia.
5. *Sample answer:* Genetic engineering is the attempt to control the DNA-protein-trait relationship so that hereditary defects can one day be corrected.

Chapter II   The Structure and Language of DNA

1. *Sample answer:*

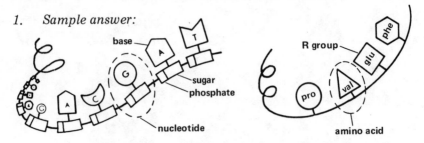

2. polymers; nucleotides, amino acids; sugar-phosphate, amine-acid; base, R group
3. four; about 20; three; 1,500 (3 x 500)
4. (1) c;   (2) d;   (3) a;   (4) b;   (5) e;   (6) f
5. (1) f;   (2) e;   (3) d;   (4) c;   (5) b;   (6) a
6. a. proline; val; glu;   b. pro-glu-glu; pro-val-glu;   c. *Sample answer:* One sequence produces the normal hemoglobin, the other sequence produces the abnormal hemoglobin that can result in the sickle-shaped red blood cells of sickle cell anemia.
7. a. mutations;   b. radiation, or certain chemicals;   c. yes (since the changed DNA is reproduced—provided, of course, that the mutation is genetic, occurring in reproductive cells, rather than somatic, occurring only in other body cells);   d. genetic engineering

Chapter III   DNA: Replication, Repair, and Reproduction

1. *Sample answer:*

Symbols like those above are used throughout this book. The structure of the bases and their actual hydrogen bond pairing is diagramed in this chapter. Obviously other kinds of symbols are possible, but ones like those above are fairly common.

2. *Sample answer:* DNA base pairing is the basis of all reproduction.
3. gene strand only; both gene and copy strands

4. *Sample answer:*

A diagram showing DNA replication:

```
 ┌A — T┐           ┌A        T┐         ┌A-T┐          ┌A-T┐
 ┌T — A┐  UNZIPS   ┤T        A├ REZIPS  ┌T-A┐          ┌T-A┐
 ┌G — C┐  ──────▶  ┤G        C├ ──────  ┌G-C┐    +     ┌G-C┐
 └C — G┘           └C        G┘ with free └C-G┘        └C-G┘
                               nucleotides
```

5. *Sample answers:* food; enzymes (in general, or, specifically, ligase, polymerase, and nuclease)
6. *Sample answer:* DNA is not really self-reproducing, since its replication requires energy, a source of new nucleotides, and the assistance of enzymes. Given these, however, a living cell or "test tube" solution with one double helix of DNA can make a second double helix of DNA just like the first.
7. a. nuclease; polymerase; ligase   b. *Sample answer:* The repair process helps to eliminate mutations that could cause hereditary defects in certain cells and, if they occurred in reproductive cells, the cells of future generations. Further, if geneticists learn to control DNA repair, they may be able to correct genetic diseases such as galactosemia, sickle cell anemia, and albinism.
8. a naked loop of DNA;   *Sample answer:* thread-like and complexed with protein
9. *Sample answer:* Because DNA is so completely dependent upon complex cell organization, it is sometimes said that "Life is the key to DNA." But even though DNA is not self-reproducing, it stores information for making more of itself and all of an organism's proteins and hereditary traits. Even small changes in DNA—caused accidentally by mutations or deliberately by geneticists—could have significant effects on future generations. Because it helps to unlock the vast potential inherent in living systems, DNA probably does deserve to be called the "key to life."
10. a. cytosine and thymine (the two bases with y's are pyrimidines) (either order); adenine and guanine (either order); b. purine-pyrimidine;   c. G: guanine, C: cytosine, A: adenine, and T: thymine

1. nucleic acid; deoxyribose; deoxyribonucleic acid
2. GCAU (any order); U (uracil)
3. messenger, transfer, ribosomal
4.

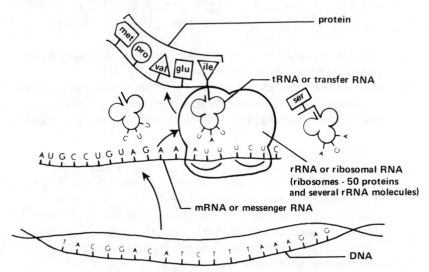

5. a. messenger;   b. messenger;   c. ribosomal;   d. ribosomal (as part of ribosome);   e. transfer;   f. transfer;   g. messenger;   h. tRNA and rRNA (either order)
6. a. (1);   b. (6);   c. (2);   d. (3);   e. (4);   f. (5)
7. Compare your answer with the following:

As the first step in producing protein, the DNA in a gene unzips from its copy strand. Then the base sequence of a gene or operon forms *mRNA* by base pairing (transcription). The mRNA segment moves from the cell's nucleus into the cytoplasm and attaches to organelles, composed of rRNA and proteins, called ribosomes. The ribosome holds mRNA, starting at the correct end, so that it can be read in triplet codons, one codon at a time. Then a tRNA molecule, carrying the codon (or anti-codon) for a specific amino acid, picks up the amino acid called for by mRNA and positions it on the ribosome by means of the tRNA base pairing with an mRNA codon.

When one amino acid is joined to another, its tRNA is
released and the ribosome moves on to the next mRNA
codon. This translation process continues (at an average of
two codons read and two amino acids joined per second)
until the mRNA segment is completed and a protein is released from the "top" of the ribosome. The amino acids of this
protein are assembled as dictated by the inherited sequence
of DNA bases. The resultant protein can then contribute to
the development of traits and carrying out of cell functions.
8. Such knowledge has helped in the discovery and use of antibiotics (streptomycin, puromycin, and actinomycin D) that
kill bacteria or stop their growth by interfering with various
RNAs in protein production. The next chapter will consider further implications in regard to genetic engineering and
the origin of life itself.

Chapter V   *DNA-Protein Synthesis: Roles of Enzymes and*
Regulators

1. a. (3);   b. (1);   c. (2)
2. a. enzyme (nuclease);   b. base pairing;   c. enzyme (ligase);
d. enzyme (activating);   e. base pairing;   f. regulator (repressor);   g. enzyme (RNA polymerase)
3. enzymes; base pairing
4. operon
5. a. repressor;   b. lactose; inducer;   c. off;   d. no
6. a. incomplete repressor;   b. histidine (his); co-repressor;
c. off; on
7. *Sample answer:* All cells have DNA for the same traits, but
some DNA is turned off in some cells and on in others—in the
way that keratin-producing "hair DNA" is turned on in some
skin cells, but not in liver cells.
8. *Sample answer:* It seems like we should be able to, since all
the DNA for regrowth of the leg is there, but we need to
learn how to turn the DNA on and off correctly. (Recent
research has enabled scientists for the first time to stimulate
regrowth of the amputated limbs of frogs.)
9. *Sample answer:* As possible accomplishments of genetic
engineers, *regrowth* of amputated limbs was just mentioned,
cloning (using DNA extracted from one cell to cause certain

traits to develop in other cells) was mentioned in an earlier chapter, *gene transplants* to replace defective genes (accomplished for galactosemia in tissue culture cells) is possible, and no doubt more things are coming.

10. a. repair enzymes;   b. viruses;   c. cloning;   d. on-off regulators (stimulated by an electric current in this case);   e. antibiotics

Unit Quiz

1. a. chromosomes;   b. DNA;   c. DNA
2. a. *Sample answer:* Sickle cell anemia is a hereditary abnormality in the shape of oxygen-carrying red blood cells. The abnormal sickle shape of the red cells can be related to an abnormal sequence of amino acids in the protein hemoglobin, which is packed into red cells. The abnormal hemoglobin sequence can be related, in turn, to an abnormal sequence of bases in the DNA molecule of the gene for producing hemoglobin. (The abnormal DNA base sequence may have started as a radiation-caused mutation, and the changed DNA in reproductive cells is copied and passed from one generation to the next, causing continued production of abnormal hemoglobin and perpetuation of the sickle cell disease.)
    b. (1) B;   (2) A;   (3) C
3. a. polymers;

   b.

	Monomer	Two Backbone Groups		Side Group
DNA	nucleotide	phosphate	sugar	base
Protein	amino acid	acid	amine	R group

4. a. base;   b. triplet codon;   c. gene;   d. operon;   e. chromosome;   f. genome
5. val-ala-asp
6. a. double helix;   b. bases;   c. *Sample answer:* interlocking shapes;   d. TACGGT (from A-T and G-C base pairing)
7. a. (1) repressor;   (2) inducer;   (3) incomplete repressor;

(4) co-repressor;   b. *Sample answer:* The genes for regrowth
of the limb or for forming hair are probably turned off. (In
experiments with plants and animals, such inactive genes have
been turned on.)

8.   a. single stranded;   b. U (uracil);   c. ribose;   d. ribonucleic
acid;   e. *deoxyribonucleic acid*

9.   messenger, transfer, ribosomal

10.   a. rRNA;   b. mRNA;   c. tRNA;   d. tRNA;   e. mRNA;
f. rRNA

11.

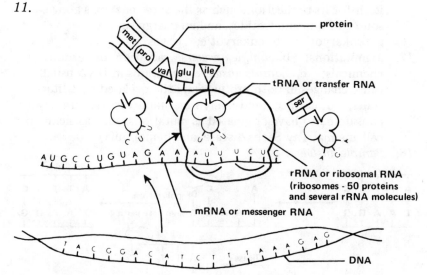

12.   a. (5);   b. (4);   c. (3);   d. (2);   e. (1) (i.e., items are in
reverse order)

13.   a. activating enzymes;   b. RNA polymerase;   c. activating
enzymes;   d. *Sample answer:* The question raised is that
of life's origin, which is usually answered in our culture in
terms of either evolution or creation.

14.   a.

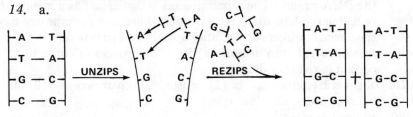

149

b. *Sample answer:* the interlocking shapes of DNA bases which enable them to form two kinds of pairs, the "rounded letter" G-C pair and the "straight letter" A-T pair (More specifically, the shapes of the bases permit three hydrogen bonds to form between G and C, and two hydrogen bonds to form between A and T.)

15. a. *n*uclease (the *n*icker);   b. *polymer*ase (the *polymer* former);   c. *lig*ase (the *lig*ater, or tying enzyme);   d. *Sample answer:* No, because DNA requires several factors outside itself for its replication, such as the three enzymes above, a source of new nucleotides, and an energy supply.

16. a. prokaryotic;   b. eukaryotic;   c. yes

17. a. mutations;   b. *Sample answers:* radiation, or certain chemicals;   c. *Sample answer:* mutations in DNA usually cause changes in both proteins and their related hereditary traits;   d. harmful (and many inheritable diseases are now considered to have originated as mutations, such as sickle cell anemia, Tay-Sachs disease, and hemophilia)

18. *Sample answers:*

or: DNA repair begins when the nuclease cuts out the damaged segment of DNA. Polymerase then zips together the nucleotides that base pair along the undamaged strand. Finally, ligase splices the repaired segment in with the rest of the DNA strand. The repair process is significant as a means of reducing the harmful effects of mutations, and perhaps one day the harmful effects of mutations, and perhaps one day scientists will even be able to direct the process to correcting certain hereditary defects.

19. a. genetic engineers;   b. (1) viruses; (2) repair process; (3) on-off regulators; (4) cloning

20. evolution; creation

Index

Meselson and Stahl experiment 64
messenger RNA (mRNA) 88-92,
    98, 100, 116
monomers 30-32
mutations 16-19, 21-22, 36-37,
    49-50; genetic vs. somatic
    18-19, 70

Nuclease 68-72
nucleotide 30-35; free 58-60
nucleus 11-13
number of bases or nucleotides
    32-33; of amino acids 40-42

Operator gene 121-122
operon 46-48, 92, 121-122
origin of life 72-73, 115, 128

Phosphate group 31-35
polymer 30-32
polymerase 68-72
polynucleotide 48
polyribosome (polysome) 97
pro (proline) 42-43
prokaryotic (procaryotic) chromo-
    some 123-125
promoter 121-122
protein 4-7, 38-43
puffs of chromosomes 118
purine 75-77
pyrimidine 75-77

R group 39-42
regulator 109, 117
regulator gene 119-125, 127-128
repair of DNA 70-72, 126-127
replication of DNA 58-60, 78
reproduction 58-60, 78
rezipping of DNA 58-60, 63
ribose 87
ribosomal RNA (rRNA) 88-89,
    92-98, 100, 116
ribosome 88-89, 92-98
RNA (ribonucleic acid) 86-88, 101
RNA virus 101-102

Sea urchin experiment 12

self-reproduction vs. replication re-
    quirements 65-66, 70
semiconservative replication 65-66
sickle cell anemia 3-5, 36, 84
somatic mutations 18-19, 70
sugar group 31-35

T (thymine) 34, 61, 75-77
Taylor's experiment 65
template 60
thymine dimers 70
traits 1-7
transcription 90, 99, 110
transduction 22
transferase (for galactose) 7
transfer RNA (tRNA) 88-89, 93-97,
    100, 111, 116
transformation of S-R bacteria 10-11
"translase" 114
translation 90, 92-97 (diagrams),
    99, 116-117
triplet codon 43-46
tyrosinase 7

U (uracil) 86-87
ultraviolet 10, 70
unknown about DNA 73-74
unzipping of DNA 58-60, 63

Val (valine) 39-42
viruses 8-9; phage 8-9; RNA 101-
    102

Watson 57-59
Wilkins 57